A HISTORY O

County Infirmary, Carmarthen, September, 1937

A History of the

County Infirmary, Carmarthen

1847 to 1948

The National Health Service

and the

West Wales General Hospital

1948 to 2004

JOHN BOLWELL & ANDREA EVANS

Noon Books
2005

British Library Cataloguing-in-Publication Data.
A catalogue record for this book is available from the British Library

ISBN 0-9549663-0-9
978-0-954966-30-0

First published in 2005

Published in the United Kingdom by Noon Books,
14 Parc-y-Delyn, Carmarthen, Dyfed SA31 1TS
Tel. 01267 234054

Printed in the United Kingdom by Gomer Press,
Llandysul Enterprise Park, Llandysul, Ceredigion SA44 4JL

CONTENTS

	List of Illustrations	i
	Foreword by the Chairman of the Carmarthenshire NHS Trust	vii
	Preface	ix
	Glossary	xv
I	Carmarthen and the Sick Poor	1
II	The Founding of the Infirmary	21
III	The First Eleven Years and the "New" Infirmary	33
IV	Patients, Nurses and the Nursing Profession	72
V	Medical Staff and the Medical Profession	100
VI	Governing, Financing and Developing the Infirmary	130
VII	The National Health Service and the West Wales General Hospital	197
	Bibliography	223
	Index	225

LIST OF ILLUSTRATIONS

Frontispiece - County Infirmary, Carmarthen, September, 1937

1 First Annual Report 25th December, 1847 to 31st March, 1848.

2 Letter of Recommendation (Admission Ticket), 1840s

3 Average weekly expenditure – 3rd April, 1851 to 25th March, 1852.

4 Architectural Plan of Ground Floor "New" Infirmary, 1857.

5 Architectural Plan of First Floor "New" Infirmary, 1857.

6 Annual Report from 1st April, 1858 to 31st March, 1859.

7 Annual Report from 1st April, 1858 to 31st March, 1859 continued with Report of Building Committee.

8 House Surgeon's Report for the year ending 31st March, 1890.

9 House Surgeon's Report for the year ending 31st March, 1890. (continued)

10 Infirmary's Red Cross Detachment at Penlan Workhouse Red Cross Hospital, 1915, Matron Linda Ditcham, 2nd row, 1st left

11 Christmas on the Children's Ward probably 1915.

12 Dedication of War Memorial probably 1920.

13 Governors' Nominating Privileges, Annual Report, 1890.

14 Private Nurses, Annual Report, 1900.

15 Diagnostic and therapeutic X-rays, Annual Report, 1920

16 The Infirmary in the early 1920s with a "Sanitary" Wing on the left

17 "Men's" Ward, 1933.

18 Nurses' Sitting Room in the Nurses Hostel, 1933

19 Nurses' Dining Room in the Nurses Hostel, 1933.

20 Rear view of Infirmary showing balcony and Nurses'Hostel on the left.

21 Infirmary Operating Theatre, 1933.

22 Carnival Brochure August, 1933.
"Proceeds in aid of Proposed Maternity Ward."

23 Foundation Stone of "New" Wing and Lady Dynevor, 14th May, 1936

24 Matron Dorothy Hartland and the entire Infirmary Nursing Staff in 1936 just prior to the major expansion of the institution in 1937.

25 The Duke and Duchess of Kent at Carmarthen Station on the 19th October, 1937 prior to the opening of the "New" Wing by the Duchess.

26 Nursing and Domestic Staff awaiting the arrival of the Duke and Duchess of Kent in the forecourt of the Infirmary on the 19th October, 1937

27 Infirmary Management Committee and senior Nursing Staff, 19th October, 1937. Front row 1st from right Mr. J.R.E. James, County Obstetrician (became a Consultant in 1948) and front row 2nd from right Dr. J.J. Healy, Consultant Ophthalmologist.

28 Infirmary Housemaids, 1938.

29 Nurses' Hostel and "New" Wing on the left taken from the balcony, 1938

30 Rear of Nurses' Hostel and "New" Wing on the right, 1938

31 Female Surgical "Nightingale" Ward in the "New" Wing, 1938.

32 American Military Hospital, Glangwili, 1942. The hospital consisted entirely of Nissen Huts seen in the background. The staff were accommodated in a separate camp of large tents and Nissen Huts which are clearly seen in the foreground behind the houses on Dolgwili Road.

33 Accommodation tents for the staff of the American Military Hospital, 1942

34 Main American Military Hospital seen from above Dolgwili Road, 1942.

35 Second World War – nursing staff, policeman and patient in the Infirmary garden, 1940.

36 Volunteers preparing dressings and bandages at the Infirmary during the Second World War, 1940.

37 Nurses' caravan parked in the Infirmary forecourt, 1947. Matron Dorothy Hartland, Sister Tutor Thomas and Della Evans currently Chairman of the League of Friends, 2nd from right.

38 State Registered Nurse Finalists, Col. W.D. Williams centre front row, and Miss E. Miles, Matron from 1948 to 1955 to his left. Della Evans, 2nd row, first right.

39 25th March, 1949 – first day on the Glangwili site. Nursing and administrative staff with the County ambulance.

40 View of Glangwili Hospital taken facing the Dolgwili Road, 1949.

41 Female Medical Ward in a Nissen Hut, 1949.

42 ENT Operating Theatre in a Nissen Hut, 1949.

43 The hospital campus in 1949.

44 Nursing staff with the first 2 patients admitted to Glangwili Hospital on the 25th March. 1949.

45 ENT section of ward with nursing staff, 1951.

46 Bring and Buy Sale, 1956
Miss E.A. Lloyd, Assistant Matron first from right, Miss A. Sim, Matron from 1955 to 1958 sixth from right and Sister Dulcie Thomas, Theatre Superintendent, seventh from right.

47 West Wales General Hospital, School of Nursing. Classroom in a Nissen Hut on the Glangwili site, 1956.

48 West Wales General Hospital, 1956 - Ward Block 1, first Nurses Home and Recreation Centre (Cambrian Room) under construction.

49 H.M. Queen Elizabeth, the Queen Mother with Matron John to her left meeting Miss E.A. Lloyd, Assistant Matron. Also in the picture from right to left, Sister P. Evans, Sister M.L. Goodfellow, Administrative Sister I.M. Emmanuel and Miss E.M. Walters, Sister Tutor. Thursday, 28th May,1959.

50 The Queen Mother meeting a patient on Towy Ward, Sister Sadie Morris to Her Majesty's left and Matron John to her right, 28th May, 1959.

51 West Wales General Hospital, December, 1965.

52 Nurses' Homes 1 & 2, 1965.

53 West Wales General Hospital, December, 1967.

54 Christmas Concert, 1966.

55 Retirement party for Mr. D.C. Williams, Consultant General Surgeon from 1948 to 1972 at the Ivy Bush Royal Hotel, Carmarthen

56 Miss Linda Ditcham, R.R.C., Matron from 1899 to 1926.

57 Miss Dorothy Hartland, Matron from 1926 to 1948.

58 Miss C.B.M. John, Matron from 1958 to 1961.

59 Miss Arfona Vaughan-Jones, Matron from 1961 to 1974.

60 County Infirmary, Carmarthen – Hospital Badge awarded on completion of training and passing the final examination for State Registered Nurses.

61 West Wales General Hospital, Carmarthen – Hospital Badge awarded on completion of training and passing the final examination for State Registered Nurses.

FOREWORD

Many of the more senior members of our community have fond memories of the County Infirmary, Carmarthen of which the West Wales General Hospital is the direct descendent.

When the Infirmary was founded it was funded entirely by voluntary contributions from members of the community it served. The senior medical staff and the administration were also volunteers. Today, this voluntary tradition is continued by the League of Friends whilst the Carmarthenshire NHS Trust, which manages the West Wales General Hospital, is financed with taxpayers' money and all members of staff are in salaried employment.

There has been no previous definitive historical study of the institutional care of the sick in Carmarthen and, as history is the basis of all knowledge, this book fills a gap. Hospital practice in the mid-19th century may seem quaint and even amusing but 150 years from now our descendents may well take a similar view of the way in which we practice acute care medicine today.

The book contains much original local research enhanced by the authors' interviews with physicians and other staff who had been involved with the Infirmary from the early 20th century. There is a concise review of the progress of medical science and of local economic and social conditions. The foundation and development of the National Health Service and its effect on healthcare provision in Carmarthen, including the current emphasis on evidence-based medicine and clinical governance, is briefly reviewed in the final chapter. The authors have not always been entirely objective but have expressed opinions which, as a practicing surgeon and a practicing district nurse, they are entitled to do but which some may regard as controversial and which the Trust does not endorse!

This history of health services in Carmarthen traces the changes and developments since 1847. Today, the NHS in Wales is involved in significant and on-going changes as high quality services are fashioned to meet the individual needs of patients. The

Carmarthenshire NHS Trust has risen to these challenges. The success of the Trust, as of the NHS as a whole, relies on the commitment of all its staff in providing a service, fit for purpose, which contributes to improving the quality of life of people in Wales.

This small volume is a fascinating read and will be of great interest to the local community. It should also be recommended reading for our healthcare professionals because it places into context our present-day contribution to the continuously evolving and complex business of hospital management and the delivery of acute healthcare to the local population.

Thanks to John Bolwell and Andrea Evans for their immense effort in producing a very thorough and readable history of hospital services in Carmarthen.

Margret Price, O.B.E., M.A.,
Chairman, Carmarthenshire NHS Trust
Carmarthen, 2005

PREFACE

In 1967 the new West Wales General Hospital was nearing completion and the Nissen huts on the Glangwili site were disappearing one by one. The old County Infirmary building in Priory Street which had provided acute hospital services to the community for 110 years had an uncertain future. At this interesting period we were fortunate to find ourselves working at all three incarnations of the institution; the old Infirmary, the Nissen huts at Glangwili and the first 3 stages of the West Wales General Hospital.

It may be trite, but true, to say that the past supplies the key both to the present and the future. Clearly, an understanding of the history of any long-term human endeavour puts the present into perspective and paves the way to the future.

We were surprised to discover that a definitive historical record of Carmarthenshire's Voluntary Hospital, the direct predecessor of the West Wales General Hospital, did not appear to exist and, as a student project, we decided to research its origins and its contribution to the development of a modern hospital service in Carmarthenshire. The first typescript was produced nearly forty years ago and was almost forgotten, until recently, when the approach of retirement provided more time for further research, revision and updating – happily, this time, using a word processor. In 2004 we found that Lesley Baker-Jones, J.P., M.A., F.S.A. had published a fascinating and detailed study in "The Carmarthenshire Historian" in 1978 which dealt with the foundation and the first ten years of the Infirmary when it was accommodated in the old Borough Gaol in Cambrian Place.

It had soon become clear that a coherent historical study could not be presented in isolation. It had to be set on a background of the evolution of economic and social conditions affecting the local community and of the progress of medical science. Politics has played a dominant part only in the last fifty-seven years but will continue to do so.

A study such as this owes much to other authors and we have tried to be meticulous in the compilation of references and in the bibliography although, because of the time lapse, we have had some difficulty in tracing some of the quotations back to their original sources. We believe that, overall, the correct attributions have been made. By far the most valuable background source has been the "The Hospitals 1800 to 1948. A Study in Social Administration in England and Wales, a scholarly and fascinating work published in 1964 by the late Brian Abel-Smith (1926-1996), Professor of Social Administration at The London School of Economics who advised successive Governments throughout the 1960s, 70s and 80s. The first 50 years of the NHS has been reviewed in encyclopaedic detail by Dr. Geoffrey Rivett in his excellent book "From Cradle to Grave. Fifty Years of the NHS" published by the King's Fund in 1997. Since 1948, the development of healthcare provision in Carmarthenshire has been directly related to healthcare policy-making by central government and this book has been an indispensable source of information.

The **Carmarthen Journal**, now on microfilm at the Carmarthen Reference Library, is, undoubtedly, the most useful primary source for detailed local information and educated, insightful opinion. Mary Bowen and Jean Gammon of the Carmarthen Reference Library have been unstinting with their help and support. In the 1960s, of course, we spent many hours in the Journal Office poring over musty copies of back issues with the generous help and advice of the Editor and staff.

The Infirmary Minute Books and the Annual Reports give a fascinating insight into the management and development of the Infirmary by the able and vigorous personalities responsible for it who volunteered so much of their capacity and time to the institution. We were greatly assisted in the 1960s by the Carmarthenshire County Archivist and Wales Herald at Arms, the late Major Francis Jones, the Editor of the **Carmarthen Journal**, by the National Library of Wales, the libraries of the Royal College of Surgeons of England, the Royal College of Physicians of London and the Wellcome Foundation, by the Public Record Office and by the staff at the Reading Room of the British Museum now at the British Library.

We were fortunate, in April 1967, to be able to interview the late Dr. James J. Healy, Quondam Consultant Ophthalmic Surgeon and former

Chairman of the Infirmary Management Committee, the late Captain K. J. Gale, R.A. former Adjutant of the Prisoner-of-War Hospital on the Glangwili site and the late Mrs. Laura Davies who had worked at the Infirmary since the late 1920s. The late Mr. J.R.E. James, Quondam County, then Consultant, Obstetrician and Gynaecologist, talked with us on many occasions and planned to make a contribution covering the years 1937 to 1967 but, sadly, did not survive to do so. He did introduce us to the late Professor Miles Phillips whose memory, unfortunately, was failing by this time.

In 2004, Mrs Tina Craig, Deputy Librarian at the Royal College of Surgeons of England kindly provided information from Medical Directories first published in 1843 and from the "Lives of the Fellows" series, which began in 1800 and is complete to 2002, with regard to the backgrounds of the founding physicians, surgeons and their successors.

We had it in mind to compile lists of Presidents, Chairmen, Secretaries, Physicians, Surgeons and Matrons. However, it became clear that it was probably not possible to be comprehensive and would add nothing to the interest of the study. The names of the principal personalities appear in the text associated with the contributions that they made which, in turn, speak for themselves.

Over the years staff and patients referred to the institution as "the Infirmary". "County Infirmary, Carmarthen" was printed on its letterhead and on the Annual Reports so this is the designation we have adopted.

The Minutes and Annual Reports of the West and South West Wales Hospital Management Committees and the Annual Reports produced by the Carmarthen and District and then the Carmarthenshire NHS Trust from 1993 are at the West Wales General Hospital and were made available to us. Unfortunately, the Trust Reports contain only brief biographies of Board members which are of little interest with few details of the senior medical and nursing staff working in the front-line and upon whom the whole service depends.

At present, the Carmarthenshire Archives hold only the Dyfed Health Authority Annual Report for 1975 to 1976 and the East Dyfed Health

Authority Report from 1988 to 1989. We have been unable to locate the remainder of the Minutes and Annual Reports of the Dyfed Authority from the 1st April, 1974 and the East Dyfed Authority from 1982 to 1992. Therefore, we have only been able to give an overview of the main organisational and developmental changes over this period albeit on a very superficial basis. Sadly, we were unable to persuade anyone currently in post with the Carmarthenshire NHS Trust, or recently retired, to contribute to the final chapter but this period, 1974 to 2004, is perhaps too recent to describe objectively. No doubt, the missing material will come to light in due course and the thirty year period will then be covered in detail by interested history buffs with personal knowledge of the "movers and shakers" of the period. The House Committee Minutes of the Infirmary from 1942 to 1948 are also still missing.

We appreciate the support of the Chairman, Margret Price, O.B.E., M.A., and the Chief Executive of the Carmarthenshire NHS Trust, Paul Barnett. The Director of Media and Communications at the Trust, David Saywell, is collecting historical material and memorabilia for eventual deposit in the County Archives. Rachel Johnstone, M.Sc. and Caryl Thomas of the Department of Medical Illustration at the West Wales General Hospital provided us with many fine historical photographs, fortunately, already archived on disk which they have expertly prepared for publication. We are also grateful to Della Evans, Chairman of the League of Friends of the West Wales General Hospital and Eirwen Bennett, former Charge Nurse at Priory Street Hospital, for providing us with copies taken from their collections of historic photographs and for permission to publish them in this book.

We are grateful to our respective spouses, Marion and Bill, for their understanding and support. Marion, for whom English is a second language, has been of considerable help in suggesting revisions of the text into, we hope, an easily readable format.

The section on the development of the Glangwili site is a contemporaneous account written by Brian F. Chudley, F.H.A. Hospital Secretary of the West Wales General Hospital, 1963 to 1967 now retired and living in Paignton, South Devon. Mike Thompson, retired newspaper editor, also living in Paignton, South Devon was kind enough to edit the text.

We are grateful to Dr. Roger Diggle, currently Chief Medical Officer of the Falkland Islands, who trained at the Welsh National School of Medicine and has a home and family connections in the area. He has a wide knowledge of the History of Medicine and of the organisation of medical care and has corrected errors and made various valuable suggestions which we have incorporated into the text. The errors which remain and the opinions expressed, which we have been unable to conceal, are solely our responsibility. Comments, corrections and further information would be most welcome. Our e-mail addresses are: jsbolwell@earthlink.net and andrea@wrhe.freeserve.co.uk

John S. Bolwell, M.B. B.S.(Lond.), L.R.C.P.(Lond.), M.R.C.S.(Eng.), F.R.C.S.(Eng.)

Andrea Evans, B.Sc.(Hons), R.G.N., R.C.N.T., Dip.N.(Lond.), D.N.Dip.

Carmarthen, 2005

GLOSSARY

ACTH	Adrenocorticotrophic Hormone
AIDS	Acquired Immune Deficiency Syndrome
AMA	American Medical Association
BMA	British Medical Association
CAT & CT	Computerised Axial Tomography
CHI	Commission for Health Improvement
CME	Continuing Medical Education
CPD	Continuing Professional Development
DMRD	Diploma in Medical Radio Diagnosis
DMRE	Diploma in Medical Radio Examination
DPH	Diploma in Public Health
ENT	Ear, Nose and Throat
EWTD	European Working Time Directive
FRCOG	Fellow of the Royal College of Obstetricians & Gynaecologists
FRCP	Fellow of the Royal College of Physicians of London
FRCS	Fellow of the Royal College of Surgeons of England
FRCS(Ed.)	Fellow of the Royal College of Surgeons of Edinburgh

FRCSI	Fellow of the Royal College of Surgeons in Ireland
GMC	General Medical Council
GNC	General Nursing Council for England and Wales
LRCP	Licentiate of the Royal College of Physicians of London
LSA	Licentiate of the Society of Apothecaries
MB BCh	Bachelor of Medicine & Bachelor of Surgery
MB BS	Bachelor of Medicine and Bachelor of Surgery
MCh	Master of Surgery
MCOG	Member of the College of Obstetricians & Gynaecologists (became "Royal" in 1938)
MD	Doctor of Medicine
MMC	Modernising Medical Careers
MMR	Measles, Mumps, Rubella Vaccine
MRCOG	Member of the Royal College of Obstetricians & Gynaecologists
MRI	Magnetic Resonance Imaging
MS	Master of Surgery
NHS	National Health Service
NICE	National Institute for Clinical Excellence
NMC	Nursing & Midwifery Council

PET	Positron Emission Tomography
PPI	Proton Pump Inhibitors e.g. Omeprazole for the treatment of peptic ulcer
RCN	Royal College of Nursing
RCT	Randomised Controlled Trial
UKCC	United Kingdom Central Council for Nursing, Midwifery & District Nursing

CHAPTER I

CARMARTHEN AND THE "SICK POOR"

On the 5th July, 1948 every man, woman and child in the United Kingdom became entitled to "free", hospital, specialist, family doctor, dental, ophthalmic and pharmaceutical services, under the National Health Service Act, 1946, which provided access to care on the basis of need rather than the ability to pay. This "free" service was financed, by central Government, from general taxation. Within 3 years of its foundation the Government introduced requirements for patients to make direct contributions towards obtaining some of these services and, subsequently, others have been excluded.[1] Society had finally accepted that it had a positive duty to ensure the health of each of its members.

The National Health Service has always operated under certain constraints. For example, it was not anticipated that its cost would increase exponentially with technological advance and the consequent proliferation of services. The dominant theme, since 1948, has been balancing infinite demand and finite resources. It was also subject to two major criticisms: firstly, that it was too strongly orientated to caring for the sick, 'a National *Sickness* Service', rather than preventing sickness; secondly, that the development of acute secondary and tertiary care hospital services was retarded by a lack of modern facilities and, consequently, a shortage of beds, often, where they were most needed.

The following pages attempt to tell the story of the Infirmary for the County and County of the Borough of Carmarthen and of the West Wales General Hospital, its direct descendent, which was the first purpose-built "District General Hospital" to be completed in Wales by the National Health Service.

On Christmas Day, 1847 the County Infirmary, Carmarthen was opened:

> *"...to supply the sick poor of the County with gratuitous medical advice and surgical treatment."*[2]

Exactly one week later the **Carmarthen Journal** announced that:

> *"The Carmarthenshire Infirmary was opened on Saturday last but up to this date no persons have applied for admission."*[2]

The reluctance of the "sick poor" to avail themselves of their newly provided hospital service raises two important questions. Firstly, what institutional facilities existed in Carmarthen for the medical care of the poor before the 25th December, 1847? Secondly, why, how and by whom was the Infirmary founded?

The very first certain instance of the institutional care of the sick in Carmarthen is by the Grey Friars, a Franciscan Order founded in 1209, who established themselves, around 1282, on the site of what is now Tesco's Supermarket at Friars Park.[3] Their original settlement was in London and became known as Christ's Hospital. After the Dissolution of the Monasteries by King Henry VIII in 1539 the establishment became the well-known school of that name which is now located at Horsham in Sussex. There was also a Dominican Order in Carmarthen living in the Priory of St. John the Evangelist and St. Teulyddog who, unlike the Grey Friars, confined themselves to ecclesiastical matters and followed a way of life based on that of St. Augustine. The Black Friars as Dominican monks became known probably settled in the town, in 1125, in what became known as Priory Street in the region of Priory Row.[4,5] In that year St. Peter's Parish Church was conferred on the Priory by the Bishop of St. David's and, until the Dissolution, the Prior continued to appoint the Vicar and pay his stipend.[4]

The oldest manuscript extant solely in the Welsh language "The Black Book of Carmarthen" (c 1250) is now kept at the National Library of Wales and was probably written by a single scribe in the Priory. It is so-called because of the colour of its binding and its association with the Black Friars. There were also monastic institutions at Whitland, Kidwelly, Talley, Llangadock and Abergwili but very little is known about them.[4]

The earliest mention of a doctor in Wales occurs in connection with the Court of the King of Wales, Hywel Dda, a Carmarthenshire man who died in 948. He is credited with the codification of the Laws of Wales although the oldest extant manuscript which refers to him dates from the late thirteenth century.[4]

The village of Mydffai lies some 20 miles to the northeast of Carmarthen south of Llandovery and the origin of its Physicians provides Welsh folklore with one of its most attractive legends. The account given by the late Major Francis Jones in his speech to the Annual Dinner of Carmarthenshire Doctors on Friday, the 1st February, 1963 cannot be improved upon. The Lady of the Lake, a water-maiden from Llyn y Fan Fach on the slopes of the Black Mountain married a local farmer by whom she had a family. She bestowed on her eldest son, Rhiwallon, the gift of healing. Rhiwallon became physician to Prince Rhys Gryg, Lord of Dynevor who died in 1234. Rhiwallon was assisted by his 3 sons all of whom became doctors. The water-maiden element may be a myth but sufficient evidence exists to show that a long and vigorous medical tradition flourished in the Parish of Myddfai.[6] The family which finally took the surnames of Jones and Williams produced many able physicians and surgeons. The tombstones of two of them, both surgeons, may still be seen in Myddfai Churchyard, David Jones who died in 1719 and his son John Jones who died in 1739. The last of the male line was Dr. Rhys Williams who died in 1842.[6]

In fact, the earliest treatise on medicine in Wales is the "The Book of the Physicians of Myddfai" translated from the Red Book of Hergest written in the Welsh language between 1375 and 1425 and now kept at the Bodleian Library, Oxford. It contains a long list of recipes, many of them herbal, for the treatment of a great variety of ailments with detailed instructions regarding quantities and preparation that was far in advance of anything else in Europe at this time. For example if you are losing your hair – not to worry:

> *"Take two spoonfuls of olive oil, two spoonfuls of honey and an onion as large as a pigeon's egg, pound them together until it becomes an ointment and anoint your head*

with it night and morning. Wear a leather cap until the hair is grown. It is best to pound the onion well before it is added to the ointment."

For treatment of a hangover you were advised to:

"Take three spoonfuls of the juice of Betony and tickle your nostrils with a hen's feather."

Trouble with haemorrhoids:

"Take smoke-dried goat's flesh, desiccate completely and reduce to as fine a powder as you can. Lay some thereof on live coals in a fireproof utensil and put same in a commode and sit thereon."

Perhaps their most famous catalogue is that of "Things that are Hurtful to the Brain:

"Gluttony, drunkenness, late-eating, much sleeping after meals, tainted air, anger, depressed spirits, much standing bareheaded, eating heartily, too much warmth, excessive watching, too much cold cures, all kinds of nuts, too frequent bathing, onions, garlick, yawning, smelling a white rose, excess of fornication, too much music, singing and reading, strong drinks before sleeping, restless sleep, too much fasting, frequent wet feet."

They emphasized cleanliness, washing in pure spring water and plenty of exercise. Much attention was devoted to the care and preservation of teeth and they recommended powders, barks and potions for cleaning them.[6] An early form of fumigation was advocated by means of the slow-burning of herbs such as wormwood and camomile on hearths to kill harmful germs![6] Their remarks concerning surgery refer, in the main, to battlefield wounds where they, wisely, state that experience had confirmed which of the treatments discussed would be most effective.[6] Research by the University of Wales and the Welsh National Botanic Garden is now underway to investigate, by means of chemical screening, tissue culture and genetics, the active ingredients of herbs still grown at Myddfai but not found elsewhere. It is also intended to team up with local Myddfai farmers to develop a commercial medicinal herb-growing operation primarily for the supply of pharmaceutical companies.

In general, outside the Royal Court and the households of noble families, physicians were rarely to be found. However, there is little doubt that, until the Dissolution and probably afterwards, monks and priests benefited their flocks with advice and herbal remedies in times of sickness and performed essential surgery. In 1092 Pope Urban II had decreed that monks should be neatly tonsured (not rescinded until 1973 by Pope Paul VI) which led to barbers taking up residence in Monasteries. Then, in 1163, Pope Alexander III banned monks and priests from shedding blood under any circumstance and thus the barbers were at hand to take over this important function.[7]

Members of the Barbers Company which was probably founded in 1308 not only attended to the hair and shaving of their customers but also bled them, a mainstay of treatment in the Middle Ages, and undertook, as necessary, general surgery, bone-setting, dentistry and the care of wounds sustained in brawls and in battle. A group of practitioners in London who did not cut hair but only performed surgery were licensed to form a Guild of Surgeons in 1368. In 1376 the Barbers were allowed to exercise some supervision over the surgeons and an uneasy relationship developed between them. In 1497 what appears to be the earliest English diploma in surgery was issued jointly by the two organisations. In 1540 the Surgeons Guild and the Company of Barbers were amalgamated by Act of Parliament and became the Barber-Surgeons Company. 200 years later surgeons were becoming more skilled and numerous and a Bill allowing their separation from the Barbers received Royal Assent on the 2nd May, 1745. The Barbers kept the building still known as the Barber-Surgeons Hall and most of the treasures and the surgeons departed to form, first, the Company of Surgeons and later, in 1800, the Royal College of Surgeons of England then, as now, based in Lincoln's Inn Fields.[7, 8]

The Royal College of Physicians of London was created by Royal

Charter in 1518 and was empowered to grant licences to those qualified to practise and to punish unqualified practitioners and those guilty of malpractice. In 1523 an Act of Parliament extended its licensing powers from London to the whole of England and Wales. The probable forerunners of the physicians were the apothecaries who originally belonged to the Company of Grocers founded in 1428 which, in turn, can be traced back to the Guild of Pepperers (wholesale merchants dealing *en gros* – hence the word grocer) founded in 1180. Apothecaries who were unable to become members of the Royal College of Physicians received a Royal Charter to form the Worshipful Company of Apothecaries in 1617. By this time, after serving a 5 year apprenticeship, they had become community pharmacists dealing mainly with the preparation and sale of substances for medicinal purposes and their status was lower than that of physicians. In 1704 the Apothecaries won a key legal suit against the Royal College of Physicians in the House of Lords which ruled that apothecaries could both prescribe and dispense medicines. This led directly into the evolution of the apothecary into today's general practitioner. In 1815 an Act of Parliament gave the Society of Apothecaries the right to conduct examinations and grant licences to practise medicine throughout England and Wales which it still exercises today.[9,10]

The Royal College of Physicians regarded the Barber-Surgeons, and their successors, as unqualified practitioners and would not allow them to assume the title "Dr". This led to the practise of entitling English and Welsh surgeons "Mr." which has persisted to this day. In fact, the state of the law respecting medical qualifications was intricate and obscure until the Medical Registration Act was passed in 1858, creating the General Medical Council, when the scientific age of medicine was only just beginning. Until that year anybody could set himself up as a medical practitioner. There were bone-setters, quack doctors and midwives in every town and village.

The wealthier members of the community had been able to obtain various treatments on a fee for service basis and always received them at home. The position for the poor at the time of the enactment of the first Tudor Poor Laws in 1576 has been admirably summed up by Professor Brian Abel-Smith:

"The main care of the sick poor came inevitably from within the family circle. A folklore or quasi-medical knowledge was handed down from mother to daughter and, no doubt, the advice of neighbours, friends and priests was taken if not always used. The patient was made as comfortable as the love and care of the family could make him. Illness was not regarded as a circumstance which required much positive action. All that could be done was to ask God to remove the affliction in his own mysterious way."[11]

The situation changed very little until well into the 19th century.

The first Tudor Poor Law Act of 1576 made each parish responsible for the maintenance of its poor. The Act directed that each parish should devise methods of gainfully employing able-bodied paupers and of supporting, by giving regular donations of food, money or clothing, those who were unable to work because of physical disabilities or old age. The Parish Vestry composed of Churchwardens met regularly to consider applications for relief, to decide how it should be given and to fix the compulsory "poor rate" that was imposed on all householders. The Parish of St. Peter in Carmarthen was divided into five wards: Priory Street and Upper Franchise, King Street, St. Mary Street, Guild Street and Lower Franchise. Each had two overseers, appointed by His Majesty's Justices of the Peace, and they were responsible to the Churchwardens for the day to day administration of the system.[12,13]

In 1723, an Act of Parliament empowered Parishes to buy, rent or lease houses for lodging, maintaining and employing the poor. However, it was not until 1758 that St. Peter's Vestry agreed to pay £15 annually for rent for the old Priory and directed the overseers to bring the poor of their respective wards to be accommodated at this place.[12,13] There is little doubt that the majority of the occupants of the new Poorhouse were elderly, infirm or disabled. The Vestry empowered by an Act passed in 1601 had, by 1620, established a "House of Correction" in the town, quite separate from the County Gaol which occupied parts of Carmarthen Castle. This House of Correction became known either as the Bridewell or the Borough Gaol.[12,13,14] It was probably situated at the western end of Spilman Street on the site of the present District Council Offices. This was where the able-bodied were to be set to hard and useful work in an effort to:

> *"...wean the naturally indolent from their deplorable habit of living on charity."*[12]

However, when John Howard, the eminent prison reformer, visited Carmarthen in 1770 he found that the Borough Gaol had been amalgamated with the County Gaol and recorded to his *"profound sorrow"* that there was very little sign of industry there. Indeed:

> *"...a number of idle and profane people were wasting their time playing tennis in the courtyard."*[12]

By 1792 both Gaols had been accommodated in the new and capacious building erected by John Nash, the Prince Regent's architect who was living in the town at the time, within the walls of the Castle – now the site of the County Offices. In the same year the Town Council was empowered by an Act of Parliament, a copy of which is held by the Carmarthen Reference Library, to build a new Borough Gaol on land conveyed by the Act described as "Old Bowling Green and Parc y Dur" in the vicinity of Cambrian Place. Pigot's South Wales Directory of 1844 confirms that this was the location. It may have opened in August, 1810. So, while the able-bodied were being subjected to *"bouts of reformative enthusiasm"*[12] in the Carmarthen Bridewell, the disabled poor were taken into the Poorhouse. If they could look after themselves, or find somebody to look after them, they remained in their homes subsisting on grants of money, food, clothing, fuel and other useful commodities given by the Parish.[12]

The Poor Law legislation made no mention of medical relief but, nevertheless, a haphazard system had evolved over the years. This was, probably, because the paupers began to realize that ill-health could be used as an excuse for soliciting or demanding "out-door" relief thereby keeping themselves out of the "Bridewell". The parishes frequently called upon the services of a surgeon or an apothecary to sift out malingerers. In 1784 St. Peter's decided to appoint a regular apothecary at an annual fee of five guineas out of which he had to advise and treat all the paupers referred to him. On the 12th January, 1802 the Parish ordered that:

> *"Mr. William Price, Surgeon, be allowed sixteen guineas per annum for surgery to all the poor chargeable to the Parish of St. Peter including midwifery and medicine and all other incidental charges that may occur in the aforesaid branches to commence this day."*[13]

These were steps in the right direction but it is hard to imagine an arrangement whereby the surgeon had to pay for medicine out of his own salary as being conducive to either conscientious diagnosis or treatment.

In 1797 the Vestry began to discuss plans for erecting a new Poorhouse and in 1799 the Common (Town) Council conveyed a piece of ground on Waundew Common and also advanced £200 towards expenses. Meanwhile the old Priory had become dilapidated beyond repair and the inmates were moved to a house in Water Street rented from one Richard Mansel Phillips. In 1803 they were moved to the old Ivy Bush Hotel in King Street belonging to Mr. Nott (father of General Sir William) who was building a new hotel in Spilman Street. After interminable discussion and delay the new Poorhouse was ready for occupation in 1805. The Parishoners had expended so much money on it that the Common Council was obliged to advance them £1,400 in 1819 to liquidate their debts.[12,13] This large and expensive building excited the admiration of a tourist who visited Carmarthen and wrote:

> *"The Poorhouse at a short distance from the town is so clean and well-regulated that it is a pleasure to see so many infirm old people comfortably lodged and by the excellent management of the Matron on the slender allowance of only four pence per day I understand they live very well.*[12]

A map drawn in 1834 shows the Poorhouse at the foot of Penlan Hill and, thus, there is little doubt that it has been on the same site from 1805 until the present day. Some of the original buildings were destroyed by fire in 1906 and had to be rebuilt.[4] The site is now occupied by the Pembrokeshire & Derwen NHS Trust, West Wales Substance Abuse Centre.

It is unlikely that this happy state of affairs prevailed much after the 23rd November, 1821 when St. Peter's Vestry directed that the Poorhouse should become a Workhouse and the 'sturdy vagabonds' who had, hitherto, been put to work in the Bridewell or Borough Gaol were sent to the institution on Penlan Hill.[2,13] It should be remembered that the number of able-bodied adults unable to find employment was growing rapidly at this time. The effects of the Napoleonic Wars were still being felt and as well as an economic depression there was also a considerable growth in population. The Parishes were finding it increasingly difficult to cope with "able-bodied pauperism" and there was a corresponding decline in the standards of care available for sick paupers. The problem was particularly pressing in Carmarthen where the slum areas around Quay Street were swarming with hordes of unemployed and destitute who had come in from the countryside to look for work. This migration of labour caused a disruption in the family system of caring for the sick and thus there was a greatly increased demand for institutional accommodation.[15] These factors were not unique to Carmarthen and led to the Poor Law Amendment Act of 1834.[16]

"Able-bodied pauperism" was to be discouraged by refusing "out-door" relief to everyone except the aged and the sick. All able-bodied paupers had to go to the Workhouse where it was intended that:

> *"...their condition shall in no case be so eligible as the condition of persons of the lowest class subsisting on the fruits of their own industry."*[16]

This principle of "deterrence" was welcomed by a Churchwarden, Edmund Hills Stacey, who became the first Consulting Surgeon to the Carmarthen Infirmary. He complained that:

> *"...under the old system paupers were not maintained in*

> *the Poorhouse but used it as a lodging house – for some time it was used as a brothel by the prostitutes of the town."*[17]

Even so, as long ago as 1794, the Parish Authorities had made an effort to make the status of "pauperism" as socially unacceptable as possible by ordering that:

> *"Every pauper in and out of the Poorhouse wear the Badges and in case of their non-compliance they are to be expelled from the Poorhouse and deprived of any further relief from the Parish."*[13]

As authorized by the Act the Carmarthen Union was formed in 1836 by the amalgamation of 25 parishes. Most of them had evolved a system of medical care although very few provided a Poorhouse or Workhouse.[17] Thus the Penlan building became the Union Workhouse. The Union was governed by Boards of Guardians often drawn by reason of the unrewarding nature of the work from virtually the same social class as the object of their efforts. Indeed, it was said that it was not unknown for the Chairman of a Board of Guardians to end his days as an inmate of his own Workhouse. However, this was not true in Carmarthen where, for many years, the Chairman was the distinguished John Hughes, F.R.C.S., surgeon to the Infirmary and one of the first Medical Officers of Health. The staff at Penlan consisted of a master and matron paid £60 per year, a chaplain paid £20 and porters and servants paid £10 per annum. In 1836 the parishes of the Carmarthen Union were supporting 400 illegitimate children so a school mistress was engaged at £25 per year.[17,18] Conversion of these wages into today's values requires multiplication by a factor of 85 to 100.

The Union was divided into five districts each with a medical officer paid £68 per annum and a Relieving Officer paid £56 a year to whom application was made in the first instance by both sick and healthy paupers.[17] Thus between the doctor and his patient *"stood the grim figure of the Relieving Officer"*. The duties of the medical officer were clearly defined by the Act. They were to:

> *"Give all necessary directions as to the diet, classification and treatment of sick and lunatic paupers and to provide requisite medicines."*[16]

- out of his own pocket?

They were, in fact, paid extra for vaccinating against smallpox (since its introduction by Edward Jenner in 1797) and for midwifery. It is evident that it was much more convenient for both doctor and Relieving Officer if an applicant for relief could be admitted to the Workhouse. Indeed, the population of the Carmarthen Workhouse went up from 91 in 1838 to 327 in 1843 about half of whom were acutely or chronically ill.[18] It was intended that the sick who couldn't manage at home should be accommodated away from the able-bodied who were being treated on the principle of "less eligibility". Such separate accommodation was never provided at the Carmarthen Workhouse where the sick were subjected to the same repressive and punitive conditions as the healthy.

The Rebecca Riots were a major disturbance in South West Wales between 1839 and 1843. The main targets of the rioters were the tollgates which were attacked by men dressed in women's clothing. The name "Rebecca" was adopted by the leader of each band from verse 24:52 in the Book of Genesis:

> *"And they blessed Rebecca and said: Let thy seed possess the gates of those who hate thee."*

The root cause of the protest lay in the dislocation brought about by the rapid increase in population and the imposition of a money economy upon a society dominated by a small caste of landowners. Attacks spread from Tollhouses to Workhouses, unpopular magistrates and extortionate tithe owners. During this period a reporter from the "**The Times**" compared conditions in the Carmarthen Workhouse and the County Gaol and concluded that life in the latter was better. The diet in the workhouse consisted almost exclusively of:

"...black barley bread, potatoes, soup and 3½ ozs of meat on Sundays and Wednesdays."[19]

In May, 1843 threats were made by local people to:

"...tear down the Carmarthen Workhouse because they starve the people there."[2,20]

Then, on the 23rd June, 1843, a broiling summer's day according to the **Carmarthen Journal**, a spectacular attack was mounted against it by "Rebecca" and about 2500 followers. The attack was dispersed by a Squadron of Dragoons from Cardiff commanded by a Major Parlby and Mr. Thomas Charles Morris of Brynmyrddin – a local Justice of the Peace. Major Parlby had told his men to take their orders only from Mr. T. C. Morris and it was long remembered that the latter had shouted to the Dragoons to "slash away" with their sabres.[2,19,20]

The rioting in South West Wales resulted in a number of Commissions of Enquiry. A House of Commons Select Committee[21] examined one Joshua Philip Watkins, surgeon to No. 1 District of the Carmarthen Union which included the town and had a population of about 12,000. Mr. Watkins considered that his district, on the whole, was a healthy one:

"The prevailing disorder is feebleness and general debility probably due to the humid climate."[21]

He confirmed that there was no Infirmary attached to the Workhouse, only a "sick" ward housed in the basement of the building, but thought that the poor of his district received good medical care – but at a loss to himself. When asked why he "kept the situation" he replied *"first of all I love the practice and secondly to prevent an interloper"*.[21] Mr. Watkins' concern to exclude competitors suggests a conflict of loyalties.

A correspondent writing to the **Carmarthen Journal** on the 12th November, 1847 (Mr. Watkins was still the Union Medical Officer) was convinced that there was such a conflict:

> *"When the Poor Law Commissioners framed laws relating to Medical officers of Unions and meted out their scanty salaries they made some calculation as to the supposed collateral advantages the Union surgeon might from his office obtain – such as attendance on Guardians, neighbouring farmers and small farmers in his district. Hence the position of the Union Medical Officer is that of a servant to two masters. The consequence is that one of his two masters must be better served than the other. That the public are the better paymasters cannot be questioned and consequently the poor are either irregularly or not at all attended to.... Ought not salaries be increased and the services of the Medical Officer restricted to the poor of his district only?"*[2]

Furthermore, in view of the fact that the sick inmates in the Workhouse were looked after by able-bodied pauper women from the adult wards who were mental or moral derelicts, often elderly, and couldn't read the instructions on a bottle of medicine let alone carry out Mr. Watkins' instructions with any degree of accuracy, his evidence to the Select Committee appears somewhat misleading. Indeed, the **Carmarthen Journal**, on the 9th July, 1847, reporting a Board of Guardians Meeting recorded that the mortality rate amongst "out-door" paupers was 6% but inside the workhouse it was 22%. The Chaplain, the Rev. D.A. Williams, was gravely concerned and demanded an investigation by the medical officers and other responsible people. The Chaplain pointed out that there had been 28 deaths in the past 6 months:

> *"The sick ward is within a yard of the Privy all the noxious exhalations from which enter the ward and must, of course, vitiate the atmosphere to a very great extent."*[2]

He demanded that something be done about the bad construction and ventilation of the basement which housed the sick ward.[2]

Leaving aside the problem of the workhouses it is probably fair to say that Carmarthen, unlike large industrial towns such as Merthyr Tydfil, did have a reputation at that time for having clean streets and reasonable housing. However, the slum areas around Quay Street were infested with miserable shacks whose filthy condition could not fail to aggravate endemic disease and where the prospect of recovery from any condition without adequate nourishment, pure water, sanitation and ventilation, not to mention comforts, was extremely remote.

It was in this favourable atmosphere, with the under-privileged and deprived yearning for a universal cure-all, that the masters of mass-psychology were able to make fortunes for themselves and fools out of a gullible public. For example, from Carmarthen to Peru advertisements could be found for Holloway's Universal Pill and Ointment. The Great Pyramid of Giza carried an advertisement for the Pill. Pills and soothing syrups were the most lucrative lines and the prescription included strychnine. At least 15,000 children were reckoned to have died in England as a result. The self-styled "Professor" Thomas Holloway left the equivalent of millions of pounds, paradoxically, as endowments for genuine medical establishments and for the Royal Holloway College now part of the University of London.[22]

An advertisement in the **Carmarthen Journal** in January, 1859 reads as follows:

The Blessing of Health by Holloway's Pills

The action of the Pills is to expel from the secretive organs and the circulation the morbid matter which produces inflammation, pain, fever, debility and physical decay and the basis of disease being removed its manifestations vanish. While ordinary remedies only afford a temporary respite to the sufferer whereas these pills annihilate the disorder.

Holloway's Pills are the best remedy known in the world for the following diseases

Ague	*Debility*	*Inflammation*
Asthma	*Dysentery*	*King's Evil*

Arthritis	*Erysipelas*	*Lumbago*
Bilious Complaint	*Fever of all Kinds*	*Liver Complaint*
Blotches on the skin	*Fits*	*Piles*
Colic	*Gout*	*Rheumatism*
Constipation of bowel	*Headache*	*Sore throat*
Consumption	*Indigestion*	*Scrofula*
Dropsy	*Impetigo*	*Stones & Gravel*

"Professor" Holloway's sardonic motto was the line from Dante:

> *"And time shall see thee cured of every ill."*[22]

It is quite evident from this grim state of affairs that there was a very real need to provide some sort of institutional accommodation not only in Carmarthen but also throughout the country for those poor rendered "destitute by sickness" or "sick by destitution" who were unable to manage for themselves. It was essential that this should be untainted by the stigma attached to the Poor Law. The respectable poor had such a horror of the workhouse that they were willing to endure incredible suffering and privation rather than enter one. The **Carmarthen Journal** devoted its leading article on the 30th October, 1846 to advocating the establishment of an Infirmary in Carmarthen in support of which it cited a visit paid:

> *"...to one of the hovels of the poor in this town consisting of two rooms with floors of clay and inhabited by a man, his wife and six children, one of whom, a girl is lying with a broken leg."*[2]

In fact, from the end of the 18th century the rich, often motivated by a genuine altruism, had seen this need and from small beginnings a great movement had led to the establishment of hospitals throughout the country. Some of the fashionable London Hospitals were venerable institutions. St. Bartholomew's was founded by the monk, Rahere, in 1123, St. Thomas's in 1207, The Westminster in 1719, Guy's in 1721, St George's in 1723, The Royal London in 1740 and The Middlesex in 1745. They were founded by religious orders and philanthropic individuals or groups of individuals. They soon began to concentrate on teaching and research and selected their patients accordingly. Some hospitals were founded by doctors anxious to specialize in some hitherto neglected branch of their profession; others by people who became interested in, or sorry for, patients suffering from a particular disease. Professor Abel-Smith points out that, in provincial areas, the process was certainly stimulated by the fact that the original voluntary hospitals were founded by the nobility and gentry and governed by persons at the top or keen to approach the top of the social pyramid. The office of President in the large London Hospitals was held by members of the Royal Family, Dukes and Marquesses. Thus, from early on, it was a mark of social status to be a member of the Board of Governors of a Voluntary Hospital.[11]

There was no question at this time of hospitals offering a better chance of cure for patients who could afford to pay than they would obtain in their own homes. The poor were glad of them in times of serious accident or when an urgent operation was required. They were certainly regarded as a preferable alternative to the workhouse sick wards but were never resorted to by the well-to-do. In many hospitals, especially the larger ones, cross infection often proved fatal to patients who, on admission, stood a reasonable chance of recovery. It was usual practice for a nurse to go around the wards with a bucket of water and a sponge to perform "wound toilet". The same water and the same sponge were used for all patients requiring wound care! A zinc tray was provided to contain the "laudable pus" which dripped from the wounds.

Patients were clearly reluctant to undergo excruciatingly painful and dangerous operations performed without anaesthesia. The surgeon wore an old bloodstained coat with a bunch of silk ligatures threaded through the buttonhole ready for use. The days of the body snatchers or "resurrection men" had only just ended with the executions of Burke and Hare and the subsequent legislation regulating the anatomists. In the 1840s these gruesome happenings were well within living memory as were the feats of the great showman surgeons like Sir Astley Cooper (1768-1841) of Guy's Hospital who once dissected an elephant in public. For obvious reasons the surgeons vied with each other in speed and precision and their popularity was judged accordingly. Sir Robert Liston (1794-1847) of University College Hospital used to say that a cystolithotomy (removal of a stone from the bladder) should take only two or three minutes at most. He was continually adding to his reputation by performing surgical feats which his colleagues declined to attempt such as his dexterous excision of a 44lb tumour of the scrotum which the patient used to carry around in a wheelbarrow. The most famous anecdote about Liston is of the occasion when he not only amputated a leg in 2½ minutes but also the fingers of his young assistant who was holding the patient and the coat tails of a spectator who died of fright! The patient and the assistant later died of "hospital gangrene" – the only recorded operation with a 300% mortality!

In 1799 the English chemist Sir Humphrey Davy (1778-1829) had discovered that nitrous oxide had anaesthetic properties but was ignored by the surgeons. Then, in October 1846, a Massachusetts dentist, Dr. William Morton (1815-1868), described the painless removal of a large tumour of a man's neck under ether – a recently discovered gas. In fact, Dr. Morton may have been anticipated by Dr. Crawford Long of Jefferson County, Georgia who performed a similar procedure under ether in 1842 but did not publish until 1849. Sir James Simpson (1811-1870), Professor of Midwifery in the University of Edinburgh first used ether in obstetric practice on the 19th January, 1847 and chloroform on the 8th November in the same year. He was actually attacked by the Bishop of Oxford on the grounds that such a technique would:

"...rob God of the honest cries of a woman in labour."

However, little opposition remained after Queen Victoria was given chloroform for the birth of her eighth child (Prince Leopold) in 1853. Chloroform remained the most popular anaesthetic until 1900 when it was realized that it could damage the liver and ether, again, came into general use.

Dr. Ignaz Semmelweiss (1818-1865), a Hungarian physician working at the University of Vienna, introduced hand-washing for surgeons and nurses in 1847 but it was not until 1867 that Sir Joseph (later The

Lord) Lister (1827-1912), Professor of Surgery in the University of Glasgow and then at King's College Hospital, London, announced his revolutionary antiseptic techniques based on the seminal work, published in 1865, of the French chemist and biologist Professor Louis Pasteur (1822-1895) at a time when hospital gangrene assumed epidemic proportions.

The History of Medicine is usually conveniently divided into pre- and post-Listerian eras and it is certainly true to say that the past 150 years have witnessed more exciting discoveries and applications in Medicine than the previous millennium.

References:

1 From Cradle to Grave. Fifty Years of the NHS, Geoffrey Rivett, 1997, King's Fund Publishing. (www. nhshistory. net Web Site maintained by Dr. G.C. Rivett and for brief overview see: www.nhs.uk /england/about TheNHS/history/default.csmx).

2 Carmarthen Journal, 1810 to date, Carmarthen Reference Library.

3 The Grey Friars of Carmarthen, 1966, Francis Jones, Carmarthenshire Community Council.

4 The Story of Carmarthen, Joyce & Victor Lodwick, 1994, St Peter's Press, Carmarthen.

5 Notitia Monastica, Thomas Tanner (revised by John Tanner), 1744, Bodleian Library, Oxford.

6 Speech by Major Francis Jones, Annual Dinner, Carmarthenshire Doctors, 1st February, 1963 taken from The Physicians of Myddfai: John Pughe F.R.C.S. The Rev. John Williams Ab Ithel, 1861. www.myddfai.com Web Site.

7 History section of www.barberscompany.org Web Site, The Worshipful Company of Barbers.

8 History section of www.rcseng.ac.uk Web Site, The Royal College of Surgeons of England.

9 History section of www.rcplondon.ac.uk Web site, The Royal College of Physicians of London.

10 History section of www.apothecaries.org.uk Web Site, The Worshipful Society of Apothecaries of London.

11 The Hospitals - 1800 to 1948: A Study in Social Administration in England & Wales, Brian Abel-Smith, 1964, Harvard University Press.

12 Transactions of the Honourable Society of Cymmrodorion, 1941, The Poor Law System in Carmarthenshire during the Eighteenth and early Nineteenth Centuries Geraint Dyfnallt Owen, Carmarthen Reference Library.

13 Vestry Registers of St Peter's Parish, 1750 to 1850, Carmarthenshire Archives Service.

[14] Transactions of the Honourable Society of Cymmrodorion, 1946 - 1947 County Gaols & Houses of Correction in Wales, T.H. Lewis, Carmarthen Reference Library.

[15] Bulletin of the Board of Celtic Studies, XIV.
The Parish Vestries and the Problems of Poverty, T.L. Jeffrey Jones, 1951, Carmarthen Reference Library.

[16] Report of the Commission for Enquiring into the Administration of the Poor Laws, HMSO, 1834.

[17] Appendix B to 2nd Annual Report of the Commissioners under the Poor Law Amendment Act, HMSO, 1836.

[18] Abstract of the Application & Report Book, Carmarthen Union, Parish of Carmarthen for the Quarter Ending Lady Day, 1843, National Library of Wales.

[19] The Rebecca Riots, David Williams, 1955, University of Wales Press.

[20] Report of the Commissioners of Inquiry for South Wales, HMSO, 1844.

[21] Select Committee on the Medical Relief of the Poor, IX, House of Commons, HMSO, 1844.

[22] From Witchcraft to World Health, S Leff & Vera Leff, 1956, Lawrence & Wishart, London.

CHAPTER II

THE FOUNDING OF THE INFIRMARY

It was against this background of poverty, social distress, a new empirical approach to the study and practice of medicine, the development of new diagnostic aids such as the stethoscope invented in 1819 and the burgeoning Voluntary Hospital movement that the matter of providing an Infirmary for the County and County Borough of Carmarthen was raised officially for the first time at a meeting of the Quarter Sessions on Wednesday, the 8th July, 1846.

County administration was, at this time, vested in the Quarter Sessions which dealt with matters such as roads, bridges, the police and maintenance of the County Gaol. This body was drawn mainly from the landed class though it included some of the County's leading industrialists, merchants, doctors and lawyers. It was appointed by the Queen's Representative, The Lord Dynevor, Lord Lieutenant of the County. The same body of men was responsible for administering justice. Matters such as education and public health received some attention but were largely left to private conscience.

The County Borough of Carmarthen (together with Lichfield, Poole and Haverfordwest it was one of the old Boroughs that remained Counties of themselves, a privilege granted by King James I in 1604) was governed by a Municipal Corporation (Borough Council) set up in 1835 to supersede its corrupt predecessor – the Common Council. The majority of the members of this corporation were also Justices of the Peace and thus attended the Quarter Sessions. Its functions were negligible until Local Health Boards were set up by statute in 1849 and the Borough Council met, on the 15th August, 1849 to form itself into a Board of Health.[2]

The main function of the Board was to provide for sewage disposal and piped water – two matters of extreme urgency and importance. The expectation of life for a British working class male in the eighteenth century was only 41 years mainly because of the waterborne epidemic infections such as cholera (there were cholera epidemics in Carmarthen in 1849 and 1866), and the greatest killer of all, typhoid. However, it was not until 1859 that Mr. E. C. Collard was elected *"Inspector of Nuisances & Surveyor"* and engineers were ordered to survey for drains and start a programme of street sweeping. Progress was slow and in 1873 the Medical Officer of Health, John Hughes, F.R.C.S., complained that morbidity and mortality rates were much higher than elsewhere in the United Kingdom because of the continued lack of clean piped water and sewage disposal arrangements for large areas of the town. Life expectancy in the town of Carmarthen was only 33 years and 39 years in rural areas of the county. He also stated that the rate of "pauperism" had doubled in 23 years to 12.86% of the population and was three times the rate for the rest of England and Wales. The main causes of death were tuberculosis, pneumonia and acute bronchitis all of which were untreatable.[3]

The terms of reference of the Board did not compel it to set up a hospital but Parliament had already authorized County Authorities to make provision for "lunatics" and in January, 1846 at the Quarter Sessions the Earl Cawdor moved for the appointment of a Committee to consider the setting up of a County Lunatic Asylum.[1] Discussion and negotiation continued for almost 20 years until, eventually, the "Joint Counties Lunatic Asylum", subsequently known as St. David's Hospital with a complement of 212 beds, opened for the reception of patients in September, 1865.[1]

The nobility were, of course, the leaders of county society and there was bound to be some antipathy to a ruling class. But there was also a great deal of respect for the gentry in Carmarthenshire and they were, to an extent, aware of their responsibility to society whilst generously supporting charitable enterprises. The greatest landowner in the County was the 1st Earl Cawdor who, in Carmarthenshire, Pembrokeshire and Cardiganshire, owned 70,000 acres. His son, Viscount Emlyn, sat for the Pembroke County seat in Parliament. The most influential family in the county was the Dynevors whose family seat at Llandeilo has links with the mediaeval history of Wales. The family had land in England as well and it was in Gloucestershire that

Lord Dynevor (3rd Baron) lived. By this period he was an elderly man and his son, Colonel, The Honourable George Rice-Trevor, undertook the difficult task of the Vice-Lieutenancy during the Rebecca Riots.

The Quarter Sessions on Wednesday, the 8th July, 1846 were discussing the form that a memorial to General Sir William Nott might take. The General had returned to the town in 1844 after a series of victorious campaigns in the Sindh and Lower Afghanistan where he had been Commander-in-Chief. He died in 1845. A Mr. William Simons said that he would place £300 at the disposal of the Memorial Fund Committee if they would agree to the money being used to erect an Infirmary which might suitably be known as the "Nott Infirmary" otherwise he would withhold it. Col. Rice-Trevor agreed that:

> *"An Infirmary was very much needed in the town but most of the subscriptions, certainly Her Majesty, Queen Victoria's as well as my own, have been made under the impression that a monument of the usual kind is to be erected."*[1]

The matter was dropped until later that day when Mr. T.C. Morris of Brynmyrddin, now the Mayor of Carmarthen (perhaps regretting his behaviour on that hot summer's day in June, 1843), got to his feet and announced that he, personally, had long been interested in the question of an Infirmary for Carmarthen and he hoped that the: *"able and influential Col. Rice-Trevor would take up the matter now that it had been broached"*. The Mayor, who with his brother William, owned a prosperous private Bank - Messrs. Morris & Sons, offered his services as Honorary Secretary if and when an Infirmary Committee was formed. Dr. John Bowen, a taciturn local Magistrate and Physician, doubted if enough money could be raised by local subscription and felt that nothing should be done until the "Lunatic Asylum" was established *"attached to which there might be an Infirmary that would, perhaps, be suitable for all purposes"*. Clearly, Dr Bowen's views carried little weight because the Quarter Sessions then decided to convene a meeting the following Tuesday at which the project would be fully discussed and a plan of action set down. As a result of that meeting an advertisement appeared in the **Carmarthen Journal** and the **Welshman** on the 17th July, 1846 which reads as follows:

At a Meeting holden at the Grand Jury Rooms, Carmarthen
On Tuesday, 14th July 1846

Resolved

That it is expedient to establish with as little delay as possible
an Infirmary for the accommodation of the Poor
of the County and County Borough of Carmarthen.

That a County Meeting be held at Carmarthen
on Saturday, 17th October, 1846 for the purpose of
carrying out the above resolution.
That Thomas Charles Morris having offered his services
be appointed Honorary Secretary.

That the foregoing be inserted in the "Carmarthen Journal"
and "Welshman" newspapers

Signed

George Rice-Trevor

Amongst those present were: the High Sheriff of the County, Sir John Mansel, Bt., holder of the oldest baronetcy in Wales created in 1621 – he was a barrister and owner of estates at Maesdeilo, Swansea and Wimbledon; Sir Grismond Philipps of Cwmgwili and T.C. & Wm. Morris. Also present was Dr. Henry Lawrence, an eminent and charitable local Physician, who had given his services to a Dispensary set up in Carmarthen in 1807 with a donation of 100 guineas from the Common Council followed by a similar donation in 1808 and which had failed some years before the Rebecca Riots because of lack of any further support.

The **Carmarthen Journal** commented on the day the advertisement appeared:

"The Bishop of the Diocese, Dr. Lawrence and Messrs. T.C. & Wm. Morris have commenced the subscriptions most munificently. Reader, go thou and do likewise according to your means."[4]

The meeting of the "nobility, clergy and gentry of the County" was duly held as advertised. Sir John Mansel was in the Chair supported by the Bishop of St. David's, The Earl Cawdor, Col. Rice-Trevor, Sir Grismond Philipps, The Misses Nott, Drs. Lawrence and Bowen, Edmund Hills Stacey, Mr. & Mrs. T.C. Morris, D.A. Saunders-Davies, M.P. for Pentre-Newcastle Emlyn, and David Morris, M.P. for the United Boroughs of Llanelly and Carmarthen.

Dr. Connop Thirlwall, appointed to the Bishopric of St. David's in 1840, in the face of considerable opposition, in England because he was regarded as too broadminded in religious and political matters and in Wales because he was not a Welshman, made some introductory remarks:

"Such as feel the prosperity of town and County at heart must feel regret and reproach that this County has been so long without such an Institution. It is to be lamented that we should be the last in the Principality to supply the deficiency. It is a duty incumbent upon everyone whom God has blessed with means, and especially on the great landed proprietors, to contribute to the building of the projected Infirmary."[4]

Swansea had had an Infirmary since 1817 and Aberystwyth since 1838. The **Carmarthen Journal** was impressed by the *"extremely perspicacious style"* adopted by His Lordship and proceeded to amplify the questions of drainage, water supply, ventilation and education referred to by the Bishop. *"It is true as well as trite"*, said the Journal in its leading article, *"to say that prevention is better than cure"* then later in the same article expressed its support for the Infirmary by remarking that:

> *"The untreated sick poor could be responsible for disseminating diseases which may be as fatal to their richer neighbours as to themselves despite the fact that Carmarthen is situated most salubriously and is, for the most part, accessible to the healthful breeze."*[3]

The **Journal** thought there was much to be done especially in the fields of health and education:

> *"Let us not be outstripped in so glorious a race by the neighbouring County of Pembrokeshire which appears to have taken up the subject with so much spirit and determination."*[4]

There was then, as now, a healthy rivalry between Carmarthen and Haverfordwest.

A local Clergyman then told the meeting that he had heard it said that:

> *"...the establishment of an Infirmary might encourage idleness, extravagance and prodigality amongst the working classes and if the humane in their generosity will provide for the necessitous in times of sickness and distress the poor will never attempt to make provision for themselves."*[4,5]

He was, of course, merely reiterating the philosophy behind the harsh application of the new Poor Laws. *"But"*, he continued:

> *"Our first object should be to do what is right and leave the consequences for we are not responsible for them."*[4]

The Meeting then thanked the Medical Practitioners of the County (there were 47 – a decrease of 21 since 1821) for the *"the kind and liberal tender of their gratuitous professional services"*. It was then agreed *"that all Medical Gentlemen residing in the County and each subscriber of £20 or £2 per annum"* should be considered *"members of the Committee charged with carrying out the undertaking."*[4]

Col. Rice-Trevor said that the basis of their plans was to obtain the use of the barracks (situated, as at present, opposite the Picton Monument) for the purposes of the Infirmary. In 1843, during the Rebecca Riots, a subscription of £2,178 had been raised from the townspeople for the erection of a barracks for the *"safety of the public peace"*. This barracks had subsequently proved too small for the purposes of the Military and Col. Rice-Trevor had already communicated with the War Office that confirmed its intention of erecting another elsewhere in the neighbourhood. The ground on which the old barracks stood was owned by ratepayers and could be bought for £100. The furniture required would cost, he estimated, about £200 and the necessary alterations another £200. As far as annual expenditure was concerned Col. Trevor quoted from the Annual Report of the County Infirmary, Glamorgan. The expenses for the year he looked into were £468 and there was an average of 25 inpatients. He calculated that if the Carmarthen Infirmary were to accommodate 30 inpatients at the rate of £10 each for the expenses of furniture and bedding and £10 for general expenses then the cost for 30 patients would be £600 per annum. A local architect, a Mr. Haycock, had offered to supervise the alterations free of charge. The next step was to secure the conveyance of the barracks by the Military to the Infirmary Committee. All the resolutions were approved and at the conclusion of the meeting:

> *"A list was handed about the Hall and in a short time a large amount was subscribed."*[4]

This list has survived and is now in the County Archives.

The next recorded meeting of the subscribers was held on the 13th April, 1847. Col. Trevor reported that they now had £3,270 at their disposal of which £1,500 was invested in India Bonds. It appeared that great difficulties were being experienced with the negotiations in respect of the barracks and their resolution was not expected for some time. Many of the subscribers were becoming disgruntled with the delay and demanded that their money be put to good use. Therefore, a sub-committee was formed to find a suitable building for a temporary Infirmary. The "medical men" were asked to draw up "Rules and Regulations".

On the 16th July, 1847 the sub-committee reported to the subscribers that the "new" Borough Gaol or Bridewell in Cambrian Place was suitable for their purposes. It had been little used since the Penlan Poorhouse was converted into a Workhouse in 1821. The Minutes of a Town Council meeting held on the 10th May, 1847 reveal that a contract had just been signed between the Council and Justices of the Peace representing the County for the *"consolidation"*, yet again, of the Borough and County Gaols. Amongst the signatories were Wm. Morris (brother of T.C.) and Dr. Henry Lawrence for the County. Perhaps it is not surprising to read in the same Minute that:

> *"The use of the Borough Gaol, free of rent, be granted to the Infirmary subscribers until more suitable premises be obtained and that notice be given to the Officers of the Gaol that their further services be discontinued and the salaries paid up to 25th December, 1847."*[2]

Dr Lawrence told subscribers that some alterations to the Gaol would be necessary – it would have to be better ventilated which meant that the surrounding walls would have to be demolished and the window apertures enlarged. William Morris stated that it would not be necessary to restore the Gaol when the Infirmary moved to permanent quarters as the Council intended to knock it down and build a cattle market on the site. Col. Rice-Trevor reported that the new barracks was not likely to be ready for at least 3 years; that the Government was paying 100 guineas per year rent for the present barracks which went into the Infirmary fund and suggested that the necessary alterations to the Gaol to make it fit for patients should be carried out forthwith. The sub-committee thought that the Gaol could be arranged to accommodate 18 inpatients and a non-resident House Surgeon or 12 inpatients with suitable accommodation for the latter. The subscribers, most of whom had had some contact with other Voluntary Hospitals – the doctors would certainly have been trained in one – wanted their House Surgeon to be resident. T.C. Morris then announced that his duties as Honorary Secretary were becoming too onerous and suggested that, when the hospital opened, they might be carried out by the House Surgeon. The subscribers disliked the idea of a House Surgeon becoming intimately involved with their affairs and, as was the custom in many hospitals, decided to appoint one of their number who had expressed an interest in the post. This was a Mr. John W. White, a Druggist, of Guildhall Square who was to be paid £20 per annum plus a commission on the collection of annual subscriptions. The subscribers also elected Lord Dynevor as the first Life President of the Infirmary despite Col. Rice-Trevor's assertion that his ageing father would be unable to take an active part in their affairs.

On Friday, the 30th July, 1847 the **Carmarthen Journal** reported that the contractor, Mr. E.C. Collard, later to become the Borough Surveyor:

> *"...had put a lot of workmen on and by this time the alterations are in a very forward state."*[4]

The walls had been *"whitewashed and coloured"* and essential repairs made to the roof and Mr. W.O. Brigstocke, a House Committee member, had painted the counters, drawers and shelves in the Dispensary.

By the 1st October, 1847 structural alterations were complete and Dr. Lawrence presented a report of the "Building and House Committee" as the sub-committee was now known, to a General Meeting of Subscribers which stated, inter alia, that:

> *"At an expense of £104.1s (out of an allowance of £200) the Borough Gaol had been converted into comfortable wards and compartments for the relief of the sick poor with requisite appurtenances for the accommodation of the House Surgeon, Matron and Nurse."*[6]

The House Committee had been extremely busy since July drawing up long inventories of furniture that they considered would be required. They had also been in close contact with Swansea Infirmary in respect of such matters as the most suitable dimensions of bedsteads, where obtainable and at what cost etc. They now asked the general meeting to approve the allocation of £400 to be expended as follows:

> *"...viz. £200 in aid of furniture, beds, bedding, kitchen requisites etc., about £100 for medicines, bottles, fixtures etc. for fitting up the dispensary – to include water pipes, washing trough and stove: and a further sum of £100 for surgical instruments, splints etc."*[4]

On Saturday, 23rd October, 1847 the House Committee decided that all drugs and chemicals should be obtained directly from Apothecaries Hall in London. Although the quality of such purchases would certainly be high it is surprising that they were not obtained from the Secretary who, as mentioned, was a Druggist. In some hospitals at this time it was laid down that preference should be given to tradesmen who were subscribers. Back in September advertisements for the post of House Surgeon had been placed in the local papers and also in the "**Lancet**", "**Medical Times and Gazette**" and the "**Bristol Mercury**". The advertisements specified that the House Surgeons must be:

> *"Unmarried and an M.R.C.S. of London, Edinburgh or Dublin and a Certified Apothecary."*[5]

The salary was to be:

> *"£100 with lodging, coal, candles and attendance found in the house."*[4]

Of the 6 candidates who were interviewed 3 were ineligible because of their ignorance of the Welsh language. Of the other 3, 2 were unsuitable and the 3rd, a Mr. W. Leyshon Thomas, refused to bind himself to continue in the post for 5 years as required by the Rules which, it was pointed out, could only be altered at the Annual General Meeting held each April. The post was re-advertised.

The House Committee met again on the 23rd November, 1847 when candidates for the post of Matron were interviewed. No previous experience was necessary! Matrons were usually selected from a "better class of person" than that which provided Matrons for the Workhouses. She had, perhaps, been a Head Servant in a gentleman's household or was a respectable widow in reduced circumstances.

There were, in fact, 3 candidates but the Committee voted overwhelmingly for the appointment of a Mrs. Elizabeth Rowlands, a widow, but then discovered that she did not satisfy the Rule which stipulated that the Matron should be aged between 35 and 50. It was remarked that the Committee should abide by the Rules as they had done in the case of the House Surgeon. Dr. Lawrence, supported by Mr. Edmund Hills Stacey, Consulting Surgeon, who wanted the Infirmary opened by Christmas, said that they *"would not be able to get on with the arrangements unless they disregarded the Rules in this instance"*. Mrs. Rowlands was appointed, provisionally, until the next Annual General meeting at a salary of £20 per annum. The only candidate for the post of nurse, Elizabeth Williams, was highly recommended by Dr. Lawrence and engaged at a salary of £14 per annum. We know from advertisements placed in the **Carmarthen Journal** that the nurse was *"not under 30 years of age and conversant with the Welsh language."* Mr. Howell Evans of Conwil Elfed was the only candidate for the post of House Surgeon. Mr. Stacey said he had given great satisfaction as one of the surgeons of the Pwllheli Poor Law Union and had also practised successfully in Rhyadr. He was duly appointed at a salary of £100 per annum – all the appointments were with effect from Christmas Day. Just before Christmas:

> *"Jones, the late Gaoler was engaged as Porter at a salary of £10 without encumbrance but with rations of the house."*[5]

Finally a board was attached to the building inscribed: *"County and County of the Borough of Carmarthen Infirmary supported by Voluntary Contribution."* On Friday, 17th December, 1847 the **Carmarthen Journal** announced that the Infirmary would be open for the reception of patients on Christmas Day and asked all those in arrears with donations and subscriptions to pay up.[4]

References:

[1] Minute Books, Quarter Sessions 1820 – 1971, Carmarthenshire Archives Service.

[2] Minute Books, Carmarthen Borough Council, (Common, Municipal, Town, Borough), 1569 to 1974, Carmarthenshire Archives Service.

[3] The Story of Carmarthen, Joyce and Victor Lodwick, 1994, St. Peter's Press, Carmarthen.

[4] Carmarthen Journal, 1810 to date, Carmarthen Reference Library.

[5] Minute Books, County Infirmary, Carmarthen 1846 to 1942, Carmarthenshire Archives Service.

[6] Annual Reports, County Infirmary, Carmarthen 1846 to 1942, Carmarthenshire Archives Service.

CHAPTER III

THE FIRST ELEVEN YEARS AND THE "NEW" INFIRMARY

On the 7th January, 1848 the **Carmarthen Journal** announced that:

> *"The benefits of the Institution are already being dispensed; this week there have been six cases entered – one indoor and five outdoor patients".*[1]

However, the **Welshman**, reporting the visit of the Bishop of St. David's on Monday, the 31st January, 1848 said that:

> *"...he, having inspected the various departments expressed, as we understand it, his disapproval of some of the arrangements".*[2]

The Gaol was a cross-shaped building of two floors and, initially, there was accommodation for 12 inpatients. Part of the ground floor was used for domestic offices and resident staff accommodation and part of the first floor converted into the sick wards. There was an Accident Ward of 3 beds, Male Ward of 3 beds, 2 Female Wards of 2 beds each and 2 side-wards. The latter were simply cells with enlarged window apertures. The larger wards were constructed by knocking down the dividing walls of adjoining cells. The walls, which were of large blocks of rough-hewn stone, were whitewashed and the stone floors boarded over.[3]

The bedsteads were made of iron by a local blacksmith and cost £1 each. Some were ordered with curtain rods attached, either for privacy or warmth, at a cost of £1-10s. The wards were heated by coal fires and lit by one hanging oil lamp and four candles. Apart from the bedsteads and straw mattresses the wards contained one table, 6ft by 2ft, with 2 benches of the same length, one commode chair for each bed, one towel horse, one large folding screen with six folds lined with green serge, one wash hand basin with ewer and a soap pan. The Committee also purchased six pewter urinals and six bed chamber pots which were emptied into one of the two privies in the yard. There was no bath until a tin one was purchased in 1848. Indeed, patients seemed averse to bathing. One hospital, at this time, reported that patients were actually discharging themselves because of the necessity of taking a weekly bath. Perhaps they had access to the "Recipe Book" of the "Physicians of Myddfai" who list *"too frequent bathing"* in their formidable catalogue of *"things that are hurtful to the brain"*.

The Matron's bedroom on the ground floor contained a "French bedstead" and feather bed, oak drawers, a table, three chairs, washstand and ware, bedside carpet, looking glass and towel horse. The House Surgeon's room was identical except for *"a little extra carpet if required"* thus signifying that his was the senior position in the hierarchy. The nurse and servant were permitted *"flock"* beds and their rooms were similar to the Matron's but they had to share a chest of drawers.[3]

The ground floor also housed the Consulting Room, Dispensary, kitchen and washhouse. The Consulting Room contained one strong centre table covered with oilcloth, six chairs, a fender and fire-irons, one writing desk and inkstand and recessed cupboards with shelves and locks. Presumably, the large oilcloth-covered table was used for operations as we have been unable to discover any other mention of accommodation for this purpose in the House Committee Minutes.[3]

The kitchen contained a large table with drawers at each end, a kitchen iron fender and fire-irons, one covered roasting apparatus, two large boilers of unknown capacity, one set of iron saucepans and an iron "fountain" filled from the pump in the yard and with a capacity of 4 gallons. Other items appearing on the inventory include: 2 doz. iron table spoons, 2 doz. plated iron tea spoons, 2 doz. tea pannikins, 2 doz. knives and forks, 2 doz. plates, 1 pr carvers and steel, 1 meat saw, 1 warming pan, 3 prs snuffers, 1 bellows and 6 smoothing irons. 16 pairs of sheets at 2/4d and 8 at 2/8d were acquired with 48 yards of towelling and 16 counterpanes. On 28 December 1847 last minute purchases were still being made - linen for bandages, tow and wadding, pillow cases, table cloths and roller blinds. Many other items were presented to the Infirmary or purchased when the need for them became apparent. The Minutes record the acquisition of such diverse items as "instrument for restoring suspended animation", a "set of pulleys for dislocations", 2 cases of surgical instruments donated by a Mrs. Griffiths, 2 stomach warmers, a pill machine, 3 yards flannel for fomentations, spittoons for patients, combs, sweeping brushes, coal hammer, mackintosh cloth for the House Surgeon to repair the water beds, a galvanic battery, 4 thermometers, a bell for the Committee Room, apothecary's scales, a pestle and mortar and a vapour bath. On the 8th December, 1848 an order was made to purchase an oyster knife.[3] Each item had to be approved by the Committee and in May, 1852 they refused to pay for Cooper's "First Lines in Surgery", Munro's "On the Nervous System" and Graham's Chemistry, Vol 1.

The Infirmary quickly had the public's confidence and the demand for beds began to exceed the number available. Sometimes temporary beds were put up even in the Consulting Room but the Committee were soon obliged to convert other cells for use as wards. Even so we read in the Minutes on the 1st May, 1851:

> *"That a room is taken this day for three months certain from Monday next at 2/- per week of William Edwards, Butcher, opposite, to be furnished with 2 bedsteads a table and chairs."*[3]

Although the Committee were assiduous in invoking a rule which provided for the discharge of patients who were not benefiting from treatment it was the shortage of beds and the unsuitable and insanitary nature of the existing accommodation that led to the appointment of a Sub-committee to:

> *"Report upon steps which it may be expedient to take for transferring the Infirmary to another site and upon the probable cost of such a transfer."*[3]

At the Annual General Meeting in 1851 it had been stated that 5 or 6 patients were being crammed into wards intended for 3 or 4 and, despite the overcrowding, cases were being sent to Swansea Infirmary. There were, as usual, financial difficulties but the funds would still run to 20 patients instead of the 15 or 16 which was the maximum that could be accommodated at that time. On the 1st March, 1854 the Rev. Dr. Lloyd visited the Infirmary and reported that the female ward was so overcrowded that one of the patients was sleeping with the nurse *"in consequence of a patient being admitted with an accident"*. It was at the Annual General Meeting in 1855 that the sub-committee was formally appointed – consisting of T.C. & Wm Morris, Rev. Dr. Lloyd, George Davies, J.J. Stacey and the doctors – but as early as the 21st September, 1853 a small group had been asked to ascertain what sites were available for the erection of a new Infirmary although no report had been made. It seemed that the legal difficulty which:

> *"...stood in the way to the appropriation of the barracks was insurmountable."*[3]

In view of the success of their venture the Subscribers decided that the erection of a new building was the answer to overcrowding.

On the 7th July, 1855 a "Special Meeting of Friends and Subscribers" was held with Lord Dynevor in the chair – Col. George Rice-Trevor had succeeded his father as 4th Baron Dynevor in 1852. The Rev. Dr. Lloyd and J. J. Stacey had examined the plans of the Brecon, Swansea and Cardiff Infirmaries and had personally inspected Swansea Infirmary. However, none of these was thought suitable for Carmarthen when the funds available and the accommodation required was considered. Six architects had been invited to submit plans of whom three (Mr. Jenkins, London; Mr. Wilson, Bath; Mr. Collard, Carmarthen) had sent in plans for an Infirmary able to accommodate 18 male and 12 female patients, capable of extension and at a cost not exceeding £2,000. Mr. Jenkins's plan had been approved by the doctors and the sub-committee and, as the successful competitor, he had been awarded 15 guineas.

The sub-committee were interested in a narrow strip of land in Priory Street (frontage 120 ft, 1 acre, 0 rods, 20 perches) overlooking the Towy Valley and occupied for 250 years by Queen Elizabeth's

Endowed Grammar School. A scheme for amalgamating the two grammar schools of the town (the other was Thomas Powell's School) was before the Court of Chancery. The ground had been valued, by George Goode, a local land agent, for Daniel Frearon, the representative of the Charity Commissioners who owned the ground, at £550. The sub-committee thought that:

> *"In addition to the building this place would be sufficiently large for an airing ground for the patients or if considered expedient it might be converted into a garden or even let to a tenant at a high rent."*[3]

The meeting was unanimously of the opinion that the Infirmary should be built on this site and empowered the sub-committee to negotiate for its purchase with the Charity Commissioners. T.C. Morris emphasized that it was essential that the permanent capital of the institution should remain untouched. The annual subscriptions were of:

> *"...a fluctuating character and it is on the permanent fund that we principally depend for the continuance of the institution so that long after we are all forgotten and mouldering in the grave the institution will be conferring its blessings on the County."*[3]

The estimated total cost of the site, new building and all incidental expenses including furnishing was £3,330. A subscription list was started for the project and passed around:

	£
Lord Dynevor	350
Earl Cawdor	300
St. David's	300
Sir John Mansel	10
R.G. Thomas	25
T.C. Morris	100
Wm Morris	50

A lengthy argument about the plans then took place. Some subscribers thought a plain utilitarian building should be erected. Others wanted an elaborate structure with triumphal arches and columns to testify to their efforts. The medical men, of course, were concerned that not only should the building be functional but that it should incorporate the currently fashionable ideas about sanitation and ventilation. As Professor Abel-Smith points out there was very little specific knowledge about the causes of cross-infection but it was believed that air and light in generous quantities was prophylactic.[4] The noble proportions of the Priory Street building with its lofty ceilings and enormous windows attests to this belief. There was a lower floor or semi-basement containing a kitchen, scullery, larder, laundry, coal cellar and beer cellar. The ground floor contained a Committee Room, Porter's Room, Dispensary, House Surgeon's Parlour, Operating Room, Dead Room, Physicians' Room, Surgeons' Room, 2 Wards and Matron's Parlour and Bedroom. The first floor contained 2 Medical Wards and 2 Surgical Wards, House Surgeon's Bedroom, 4 Staff Bedrooms and a Supplemental Ward. It is interesting to note that the lavatories for the surgical patients were outside their ward unlike those for the medical patients. Furthermore, they were siphon-type water closets emptying through drainage pipes into a cesspit at the back of the garden. There was gas-lighting throughout and two lifts for raising food, medicine, clothes and coal. In 1883, Dr. Oppert said:

> *"The usefulness of lifts is beyond doubt although as regards patients they are necessary in consumption hospitals but I should not consider them of paramount necessity in general hospitals; they are not even much used where they exist."*[5]

It is probably fair to say that the building did measure up to the highest standards of the day. The water closets and gas-lighting were certainly modern at the time.

The plans were debated and amended for almost two years until, on the 7th January, 1857 another Special Meeting approved the final modification of Mr. Jenkins's plans and invitations to tender were placed in national as well as local newspapers. At the Annual General

Meeting in 1857 Dr Henry Lawrence reported on behalf of the Building Committee:

> *"The consideration money was paid on the 7th February last when the purchase was duly completed and possession of the premises delivered up. Two tenders only have been sent in both of which are below Mr. Jenkins' estimate. One of them from a builder in Bristol is not accompanied as required by the names of two respectable persons willing to become security for the due performance of the works. The other tender is from Mr. William Lewis of Carmarthen and the Building Committee recommend that it should be accepted subject to Mr. Lewis engaging to use Aberddaw lime in all the external walls of the building which are not to be covered with cement. Assuming the acceptance of Mr. Lewis's tender the foundation stone of the new Infirmary may be laid on or about the 28th inst. And the Building Committee begs to submit to the General Meeting whether so important and interesting event should not be celebrated by an appropriate inauguration."*[1]

The Bishop of St. David's thought that it should and that a collection *"on the ground"* would be advisable. Furthermore, if they had a *"procession it would, no doubt, bring a number of persons together and those who had not subscribed to the fund might do so then."* There was a large and influential body of Freemasons in the town who might possibly be *"inclined to attend and it would have the effect of bringing a number of brethren together and make a corresponding increase in the funds."* The Provincial Grand Master, John Johnes of Dolaucothi an eminent lawyer, just happened to be at the meeting and he promised to try and arrange the participation of the Freemasons subject to the approval of the Grand Lodge of England. It was decided, if nothing occurred to prevent it, that the first stone should be laid on the 14th May, 1857.[1]

The **Carmarthen Journal** reported the events in characteristic style:

> *"At one o'clock the Corporation and nearly all the*

respectable inhabitants of the town met in the Guildhall and shortly afterwards formed themselves into a procession in the following order:

Band of Music, Carmarthen Brass Band
Chief Constable
Constables two-a-breast
Hall Keeper
Mace Bearer
Town Clerk, Mayor and Sheriff
Aldermen two-a-breast
Common Councilmen two-a-breast
Architect
Building Committee two-a-breast
Clergymen ditto
Dissenting Ministers ditto
The Choir of St. Peter's Church two-a-breast
Students of Training College ditto
Subscriber's ditto
Inhabitant's ditto

The procession passed up Lower Market Street, Nott Square and Queen Street and were then joined opposite the Ivy Bush by the Freemasons (attired in the costume peculiar to the order) thence proceeding up Spilman Street, Church Street and Priory Street to the doorway leading to the building. On the arrival of His Lordship (the Bishop) at two o'clock the procession filed off permitting him and the Masons to pass up through the centre on to the site of the new building which is situate at the entrance to the Parade from Priory Street on the land occupied until a few weeks since by the Queen Elizabeth's Endowed Grammar School. The new building will be erected on the playground behind the schoolroom which has not yet been removed. Mr. Lewis, the contractor, in his anxiety to complete the work as speedily as possible having already raised part of the walls several feet a large part of the front of the building was appropriated for a platform, the timber stretching from one wall to the other, supplied a large area, which was occupied exclusively by the male portion of the assembly. At the southwest corner where the foundation stone was laid a chair was placed for the Bishop facing a flight of stairs covered with baize. At the back of the old school building and of an abutting house were raised seats in the form of an amphitheatre occupied by ladies who imparted a grace and brilliancy to the assembly which contributed greatly to its imposing appearance. Between the platform and these raised seats was an avenue occupied by the Freemasons who clustered around the foundation stone so as to obscure the view of those immediately behind them. The scene was most gratifying although not as striking as many we have witnessed in the town. But in compensation for any deficiency of splendour there was a calm dignity combined with a radiant benevolence more satisfying to the mental eye than a coup d'oeil of other descriptions."[1]

A religious service was held and after the singing of the Hundredth Psalm and a prayer *"coins of the realm"* were deposited in a hollowed-out portion of the foundation stone. Along with these was placed a bottle containing the following statement *"very tastefully written on vellum"* by Alcwyn C. Evans, the amateur historian, who, as a boy of 15 witnessed the attack on the workhouse in 1843. Much of his work is preserved in manuscript in the National Library of Wales.[6]

The Foundation Stone
Of the
Infirmary

For the use of the County and County of the Borough
of Carmarthen was laid on Thursday, the fourteenth day
of May, in the year of our Lord one thousand, eight
hundred and fifty seven and in the twenty first year
of the reign of Her Majesty Queen Victoria

by

Connop, Lord Bishop of St David's
In the seventeenth year of his Episcopate

The Lord Dynevor	President
Henry Lawrence Esq.	Physician
Edmund Hills Stacey Esq.	Consulting Surgeon
John Hughes Esq.	Surgeon
James Rowlands Esq.	Surgeon
Geo. S. Symmons Esq.	House Surgeon
Thomas Charles Morris	Treasurer
William Morris	Treasurer
William Wesley Jenkins	Architect
William Lewis	Builder
John W. White	Secretary

"The Lord Bishop, after trying the stone with the level, plumb, rule and square gave it three taps and pronounced it well and truly placed. The Grand Master then, according to ancient custom, poured wine and oil on the topstone then laid. The proceedings attendant upon this ceremony were exceedingly simple in perfect keeping with the Institution. There was no garish splendour or gaudy show. Everything was quietly and orderly done, and the event altogether characterized by an air of respectability and unobtrusive enthusiasm which must have gratified all who witnessed it. Fortunately, the weather was most propitious if we except the unpleasantness of exposure with uncovered heads to the burning sun for more than an hour whilst the service was progressing. However, the fineness of the weather induced a large attendance."[1]

The man from the **Welshman**, however, had a complaint:

"It is not often that reporters are on such occasions provided with proper accommodation at meetings in this town. We, therefore, appreciate the attention of Mr. Goode in setting apart a place for them but there being no barrier at the back of the seat the assembly pressed upon

> *those engaged in taking notes with such violence that it was at any time very difficult to write and frequently impossible for two or three minutes to do so at all; even when standing up, book in hand, bending over the desk to avoid serious injury from the crowd."*[2]

At the conclusion of the ceremony the Bishop made an interesting and important speech:

> *"Of late years it has been more strongly felt than ever that Institutions of this nature are labouring under one grievous defect...... in many instances, unfortunately, persons of this class (hireling nurses) are actuated by mercenary motives having no heart or goodwill in their work apparently feeling themselves bound to do no more for the comfort of the patients committed to their care than they are compelled to do and being really indifferent to their welfare and happiness. This is an evil which has long been felt and we have occasion to thank God that some steps have effectually been adapted to remedy it. We are indebted for this better state of things mainly to the energy and devotion of an illustrious lady who, with an unparalleled degree of self-sacrifice left her luxurious English home and, amidst the greatest privation, ministered to the suffering and sick of her fellow-countrymen by their loathsome beds in the inefficient hospitals at Scutari."*[1]

Battle casualties from the Crimean War (1854 to 1856) were evacuated to the British Military Hospitals in Scutari, Turkey where Florence Nightingale and her team of 38 lady nurses were based.

> *"It is to do honour to that illustrious lady, Miss Nightingale, (applause and sensation) that an attempt has been made to form a permanent establishment for the training of able and experienced nurses and the result of the glorious efforts that have been made has been the erection of a Central Institution which, in the process of*

time, will supply those who will really deserve that name of Nurse to the sick and who will be fully competent and able to discharge the duties of their sacred office. For unless it is felt to be a sacred office no efficient aid can be expected from this class of persons. And, therefore, above all things, my wish is that when the building of the Infirmary shall have been accomplished it may not want for an efficient staff of female officers, trained and experienced female nurses who would no less from duty than inclination devote their time and labour to the sick and afflicted."[1]

This speech is remarkably prescient because it was to be nearly thirty years before the Infirmary was able to boast a trained Matron and more than 60 years before the Nurses Act of 1919 established the General Nursing Council for England and Wales and the state registration of nurses although doctors were required to be registered from 1858 and midwives from 1902.

Construction proceeded apace and by January, 1858 the new 30 bedded Infirmary had nearly been completed. But, as so often happens, costs exceeded estimates and the special building fund became exhausted. The Committee was obliged to call a special meeting of subscribers on the 24th January and, despite their efforts to avoid encroaching on the permanent capital of the institution, had to ask that the:

"The Treasurer be authorized under the direction of the Building Committee to sell out so much of the capital of the institution invested in India bonds as may be required to complete the Infirmary premises and to furnish the Building."[3]

On the 30th June, 1858 an entry in the Minute Book reads:

"Ordered that the House Surgeon make arrangements for removing the establishment to the New Infirmary as soon as possible."[3]

Then, on the 7th July, 1858 under the proud legend *"Carmarthenshire New Infirmary"*[3] we read:

> *"Nicholas & Daniel, carters removing £1. 0s. 0d.*
> *Ale for men removing 6s. 6d."*

> *"ordered that the Matron do employ a charwoman once a fortnight to assist in cleaning out the Infirmary."*[3]

There was also a copy of a letter sent to the Town Council expressing:

> *"The deep sense the House Committee entertain of the kindness and liberality of the Town Council in permitting the institution to have the gratuitous use of the Borough Gaol for more than 10 years."*[3]

During the week the move took place there were 11 in-patients and 50 out-patients on the books.

Having expended so much money on the new building the Committee were obliged to redouble their efforts to obtain more subscribers to keep the Infirmary open. Three hundred letters of appeal were printed and distributed by the police. Advertisements appeared in local papers, contribution boxes were placed in taverns, hotels and on pedestals throughout the town. A letter was sent to Mr. H. Brinley Richards, who was to compose that patriotic ditty "God Bless the Prince of Wales" asking if he would give a concert during Race Week.[3]

A sharp eye was kept on expenditure. On the 8th November, 1858 the attention of the "*...medical men is called to the consumption of gas in the Infirmary with a view to economise."*[3] Most of the furniture came from the Gaol although the Committee did spend £70 on equipping the new Operating Room, Dead Room and Committee Room. The old laundry boiler was to be erected in the new building provided an endorsement could be obtained on the policies of insurance "*...to the effect that same will not be vitiated by so doing."* The Committee also invested in 3 large sweeping brushes, 1 stair brush, 1 iron bound box with handles for ashes, 2 counterpanes for the House Surgeon's bed and 20 brass hooks for cards over patients' beds.[3]

The Committee were not prepared to let the need for thrift interfere with its public image. By November, 1858 a labourer had been employed for levelling the ground, a kitchen garden was started at the back of the building, ornamental shrubs had been ordered for the front garden and the inscription on the front of the building was replaced and the letters gilded.[3]

The total expenditure on building and equipping the new Infirmary was £4,565 10s. 6d. A breakdown of that amount appeared in the Annual Report for the year ending April, 1859.[7] The Committee point out in their report that the new building was:

> *"...capable of accommodating a much larger number of patients than their funds allow them to receive."*[7]

The Committee were sufficiently confident about their new building to:

> *"Earnestly invite gentlemen residing in this or neighbouring counties to visit the establishment that they may see how well adapted it is to carry out most fully its noble and benevolent objects."*[7]

Thus the Infirmary for the County and County of the Borough of Carmarthen came into being at the beginning of the most exciting era in the History of Medicine. After surviving for 11 years in singularly unsuitable and insanitary accommodation it moved to purpose-built premises in Priory Street the façade of which still exists. The Infirmary's services to the community were to continue with increasing scope and efficiency for more than a century, until on the 5th July, 1948 the voluntary hospitals movement was eliminated by the National Health Service Act.

References:

[1] Carmarthen Journal, 1810 to date, (Microfilm), Carmarthen Reference Library.
[2] The Welshman, 1832 to 1945, (Microfilm), Carmarthen Reference Library.
[4] The Hospitals - 1800 to 1948: A Study in Social Administration in England & Wales, Brian Abel-Smith, 1964, Harvard University Press.
[5] Hospitals, Infirmaries and Dispensaries, F. Oppert, M.D., London, 1883.
[6] Manuscript History of the Borough of Carmarthen, Alcwyn C. Evans, 1867, NLW MS 12369-71B, National Library of Wales.
[7] Annual Reports, County Infirmary, Carmarthen, 1846 to 1942, Carmarthenshire Archives Service.

CARMARTHENSHIRE INFIRMARY,

SUPPORTED BY VOLUNTARY CONTRIBUTIONS.

THE OBJECT OF THE INSTITUTION BEING TO AFFORD MEDICAL AND SURGICAL RELIEF TO THE SICK POOR.

President.

LORD DYNEVOR.

Vice-Presidents.

HON. COLONEL RICE TREVOR, M.P.
SIR JOHN MANSEL.
W. CHAMBERS, ESQ., SEN.
W. CHAMBERS, ESQ., JUN.
THOMAS CHARLES MORRIS, ESQ.
WILLIAM MORRIS, ESQ.
THE LORD BISHOP OF ST. DAVID'S.
J. COLBY, ESQ.
MAJOR GENERAL SIR JAMES COCKBURN.
EARL CAWDOR.
DAVID SAUNDERS DAVIES, ESQ., M.P.
CHARLES MORGAN, ESQ., M.D.
DAVID MORRIS, ESQ., M.P.
THOMAS MORRIS, ESQ.
R. J. NEVILL, ESQ.
MESSRS. WILKINS & CO.
J. WALTERS PHILIPPS, ESQ.
MR. JUSTICE VAUGHAN WILLIAMS.
GEORGE MORGAN, ESQ.
LLOYD VAUGHAN WATKINS, ESQ.
HENRY LAWRENCE, ESQ., M.D.
J. W. G. HUGHES, ESQ.
RICHARD RICHARDS, ESQ.
W. O. BRIGSTOCKE, ESQ.
E. R. WOOD, ESQ.
DOCTOR JONES.

Physicians.

DOCTOR BOWEN. | DOCTOR LAWRENCE.

Surgeons.

MR. HUGHES. | MR. ROWLANDS.

Treasurers—MESSRS. MORRIS & SONS. | *Secretary*—MR. J. W. WHITE.

AT the MEETING of the SUBSCRIBERS, held at the TOWN HALL, on FRIDAY, the 7th Day of APRIL, 1848, the following REPORTS were presented:—

TREASURERS' REPORT.

RECEIPTS.

	£	s.	d.
Donations Received	1322	9	0
Yearly Subscriptions	470	10	0
Straw Sold	0	4	6
Rent of Barracks	164	1	0
Balance due to the Treasurers	16	4	6
	£1973	9	0

EXPENSES.

	£	s.	d.	£	s.	d.
Paid Mr. Collard for altering Borough Goal for the purpose of a Temporary Infirmary	104	1	0			
Subsequent Mason's and Carpenter's Work for ditto	5	14	11			
Painting, &c.	9	1	10			
				118	17	9
Furniture, Fittings, Iron Bedsteads, Bedding, and other requisites for furnishing House				164	5	3½
Drugs, Chemicals, Bottles, and Surgical Instruments				77	15	0
Diet for Patients and Servants				21	19	5½
Coal, Wood, Candles, &c.				10	2	10½
Advertising				40	5	6
Paid for Copying Rules & Regulations				1	1	0
Stationery and Printing				15	17	[illegible]
Wages to Jones, late Porter, and Charwomen				3	7	0
Postages and Post Office Orders				1	2	10
Contingencies				2	5	10
				456	19	8
Balance remaining in Secretary's hand for small disbursements				1	4	5
				458	4	1
By £500 India Bonds bought				506	18	11
By £1235 5s. 7d. Consols purchased in the names of the Trustees				1008	6	0
				£1973	9	0

	£	s.	d.	
Permanent Capital of the Institution	1235	5	7	Consols
Floating Capital in India Bonds	500	0	0	

In presenting to the Subscribers of the CARMARTHENSHIRE INFIRMARY a Report for the last four months, commencing on the 25th of December, 1847, there is much to which the Committee have to direct special attention; they can assert with confidence that this excellent Institution is progressing most satisfactorily towards efficiency, that the Rules have been carried out in accordance with the spirit of its founders, and that it is gratifying to know that the advantages it affords are most gratefully acknowledged by the poorer classes; the number of In-Door Patients who have been admitted amounts to 15, the number of Out-Patients to 90. It has at all times been the anxious wish of the Committee to extend as widely as possible the benefits of the Infirmary, and in accordance with this feeling, and encouraged by the liberal contributions of the friends of the Institution, Fourteen Beds are prepared for the reception of the Sick in the House, and of Out-Patients an unlimited number are admitted; and they trust that when the distant parts of the County are made acquainted with the progress of the Institution it will become more generally useful.

The Committee have been constant in their attendance, and hope the Subscribers generally will be satisfied with their exertions.

Slight alterations of some of the Rules will be submitted to the Meeting for their approval, together with a proposition respecting the Secretary's Salary, and a recommendation that he be paid a commission of 5 per cent on the collection of the Yearly Subscriptions as customary in other similar institutions, such allowance to commence retrospectively.

THOMAS JONES, M.D., CHAIRMAN.

H. WHITE AND SONS, PRINTERS, CARMARTHEN.]

Admission day in future will be Thursday

1. First Annual Report 25th December, 1847 to 31st March, 1848.

CARMARTHENSHIRE INFIRMARY,

SUPPORTED BY VOLUNTARY CONTRIBUTIONS.

The LETTER *to recommend* In *and* Out-Patients.

Gentlemen,

I recommend the bearer *residing at*

for an

Patient if the Board shall consider h *a proper object of the Charity.*

day of 184

Your humble Servant,

To the Governors

Contributors are desired to observe the following Articles: *viz.*

I. Recommendations are to be delivered every *Wednesday* morning by half-past Eleven of the clock, and *none* will be received *after* that time.

II. When there is not room in the House for all the Patients recommended at one time to be received, *those* only are admitted, who, the Board is of opinion, will most effectually answer the ends of the Charity; and the rest, if proper objects, are admitted Out-Patients till there is a vacancy in the House.

III. No person labouring under any infectious distemper, deemed incurable, or whose case is consumptive or asthmatic, or having old ulcerated legs, more proper for a workhouse is to be received into the House.

IV. On account of the number of Contributors each Governor can have but *one* In-patient at a time, Subscribers of *three* guineas are allowed to recommend *three* In-patients every year; and no Governor can have more than *two* Out-patients on the books at one time.

V. Each Patient, if able, to bring two shirts or shifts, but Patients are not required to find themselves with *Provisions of any kind* during their stay in the Hospital.

VI. If any Nurse or Servant receive any money, treat, present, or gratuity, either from a Patient, or any relation or friend of such Patient, or from any other person, in respect for the services of such Nurse or Servant in the Hospital, such Nurse or Servant shall be dismissed.

The Contributors are requested to send their money to this Hospital upon any Wednesday, *from Ten till Three.*

***** The large number of surgery Patients requiring a great quantity of Lint and Cloth for rollers, &c. if Ladies please to send in some old linen, it will be a valuable present to the Charity.**

2. Letter of Patient Recommendation (Admission Ticket) 1840s

Abstract of the Averages of the weekly expenditure of the County and County of the Borough of Carmarthen Infirmary for One year commencing the 3rd of April 1851 to the 25th of March 1852 — Shewing the average cost per head, and the average consumption of Animal Food, Flour and Potatoes. —

Quarter ending	Weekly average of Inmates	Weekly Total expenditure	Weekly expenditure per Head	Weekly average of Flour	Weekly average Flour per Head	Weekly average of Butchers Meat	Weekly average of Butchers Meat per Head	Weekly average of Potatoes	Weekly average of Potatoes per Head
1851		£ s d	s d	lbs ozs	lbs ozs	lbs ozs	lbs ozs	lbs ozs	lbs ozs
June 26	16½	3 · 9 · 9	3 · 9¼	86 · 2	4 · 10½	59 · 12	3 · 3½	114 · —	6 · 2
Sept 25	18¼	3 · 6 · 1¼	3 · 1¾	93 · —	5 · 1½	63 · —	3 · 7¼	91 · 8	5 · —
Dec 25	18	3 · 6 · 4¾	3 · 8¼	86 · 8	4 · 13	64 · 7	3 · 9	112 · —	6 · 4
1852 Mar 25	17½	3 · 7 · 5¼	3 · 11	89 · 3	5 · 3	61 · 11	3 · 9	120 · 9	7 · 1

E. Stacey   G. W. Bagnall   John M. White

3. Average weekly expenditure – 3rd April, 1851 to 25th March, 1852.

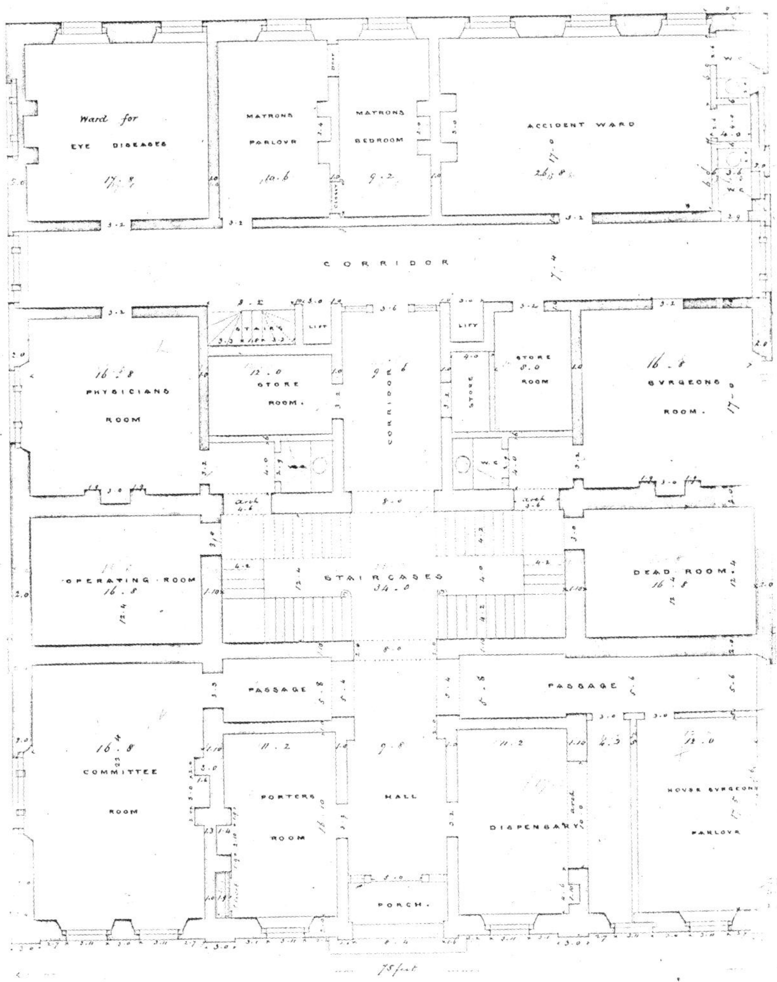

4. Architectural Plan of Ground Floor "New" Infirmary, 1857.

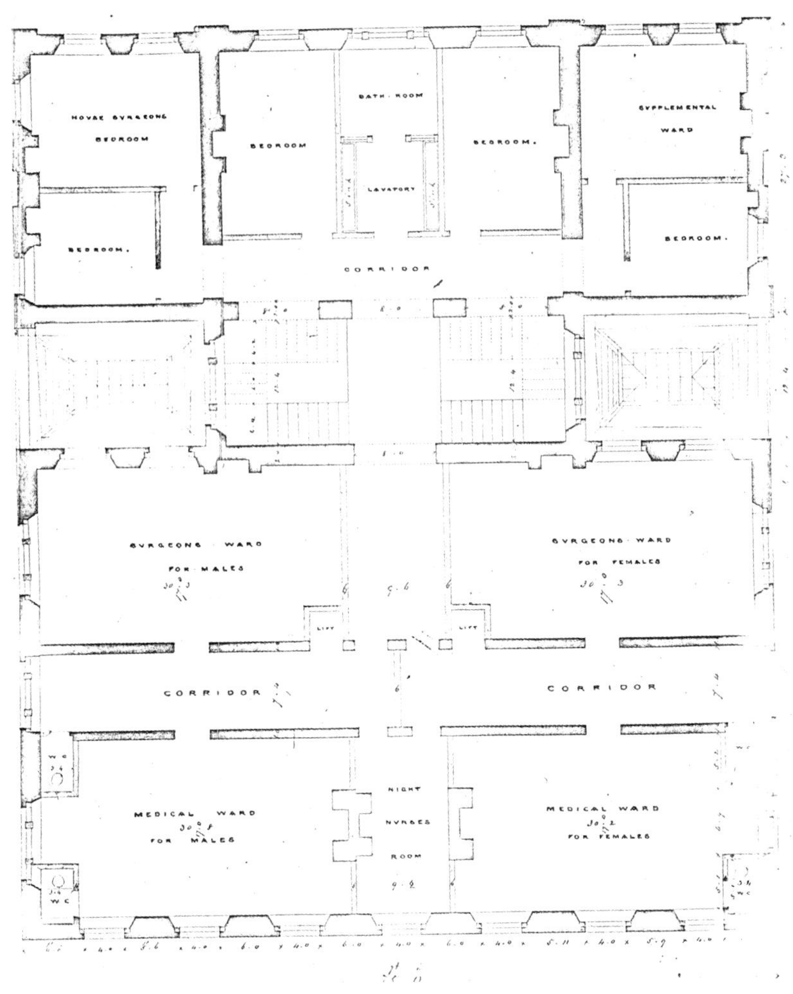

5. Architectural Plan of First Floor "New Infirmary, 1857.

COUNTY AND COUNTY OF THE BOROUGH

OF

CARMARTHEN INFIRMARY.

AT the TWELFTH ANNUAL MEETING of the GOVERNORS and SUBSCRIBERS, held at the GUILDHALL, CARMARTHEN, on Friday, the 8th of APRIL, 1859,

SIR JOHN MANSEL, BART., IN THE CHAIR.

THE FOLLOWING REPORTS WERE PRESENTED:—

THE TREASURER'S REPORT from the 1st of APRIL, 1858, to the 31st of MARCH, 1859, INCLUSIVE

—o—

RECEIPTS.

	£	s.	d.
To Annual Subscriptions received	382	3	6
Sundry Donations	40	7	0
Sundry Fines and Penalties received on behalf of the Infirmary	5	10	0
Collections at St. Thomas's Chapel, Ferry	7	9	3
Do. at Llanstephan Church, by the Rev. B. Evans	9	0	0
Do. at Llanarthney Church	1	5	0
Proceeds of a lecture on Phrenology, delivered by Dr Lloyd	7	0	0
Collection at Llanboidy Church, by the Ven. Archdeacon Evans	1	13	0
Moiety of do. at Llanglydwen Church, by do.	0	11	6
Collection at St. David's Church, Carmarthen	8	10	0
Do. at St. Peter's Church, by Ven. Archdeacon Bevan	15	3	0
Do. at Llangendeirne Church, by Rev. D. Jones	0	13	6
Do. at Llandefeilog Church, by Rev. H. Roberts	4	17	0
Do. at Abergwilly Church	9	4	3
Do. at the Welsh Wesleyan Chapel	0	14	0
Do. at Llanegwad Church, by the Rev. E. Evans	2	0	0
Do. at the Catholic Chapel, by Rev. L. Havard	0	8	3
Income Tax returned on Consols and India Bonds to July 1858	5	3	2
Cash from Contribution Boxes in Infirmary	0	11	0
Dividend on Consols	77	14	2
Interest on India Bonds	38	18	0
Transfer from Building Fund, for the purposes of Furnishing	70	0	0
	£688	15	7
Balance brought forward	12	17	11

EXPENDITURE.

	£	s.	d.
By Balance due to the Treasurers from last year	57	17	3
Medicines, &c	82	14	6
Diet	207	5	7
Repairs, Furniture, &c	63	4	10
Printing, Advertising, and Stationary	19	6	10
Coal, Firewood, and Candles	30	5	7
Salaries	235	3	2
Contingencies paid for, Labour, Laying out the Grounds, &c	19	19	11
Balance carried forward	12	17	11
	£688	15	7

Permanent Capital of the Institution : Consols £2606 10 8
Floating Capital : India Bonds £400 0 0

We have examined this account, and find it correct, leaving a balance of £12 17s. 11d. due to the Infirmary in the hands of the Treasurers.

J. J. STACEY,
GEO. BAGNALL, } Auditors.

6. Annual Report from 1st April, 1858 to 31st March, 1859.

REPORT OF THE HOUSE COMMITTEE.

The Committee feel much satisfaction in being able to continue to report favourably of the efficiency of the Infirmary, and desire to direct public attention to the fact that the New Building, which has been occupied since 1st of July, 1858, is capable of accommodating a much larger number of Patients than the present state of their Funds allows them to receive. They feel assured that this circumstance needs only to be known in order to call forth the liberality of those who either by property or residence are connected with the County and Borough of Carmarthen. The Committee would earnestly invite gentlemen residing in this or in the neighbouring Counties to visit the Establishment, that they may see how well adapted it is to carry out most fully its noble and benevolent objects. The Committee, therefore, appeal with confidence to all who are interested in such charitable Institutions, for continued and increased support.

The Committee beg to acknowledge publicly the gratuitous and important services of the Physician and Surgeons connected with the Establishment.

The Committee desire also gratefully to acknowledge the increased exertions of the Clergy and Ministers of various denominations on behalf of the Infirmary.

The Committee desire also publicly to acknowledge the munificent addition made to the funds of the Establishment, by Sir James Williams, Bart., who has generously devoted the sum of Forty Pounds annually for the next seven years, being the amount of rental arising from the Game on the Derllys Estate.

The Committee desire further to express their thanks to the Rev. Dr. Lloyd, for Seven Pounds, being the proceeds of a Lecture delivered by him in aid of the funds of the Infirmary.

The number of Inn-door Patients admitted during the last year was....		72
Out of which died..	3	
Cured and relieved..	52	
Remaining in the House	17	
	—	72
The number of Out-door Patient, admitted during the last year was...		329
Out of which died..	7	
Cured and relieved..	271	
Remaining	51	
	—	329

GEO. BAGNALL, Chairma.

The Carmarthenshire Infirmary Building Committee beg leave to present an account of the receipts and expenditure connected with the erection of the New Infirmary. They have the satisfaction of stating that the Building has now been completed in all respects, and they believe that it is admirably adapted to the purposes for which it is required, and that the work has in every particular been well done.

The functions of the Committee have now ceased, and in this their final report they have only to express a hope that the Institution may continue to prosper, and that it may receive an adequate measure of support from those who have the ability of contributing to its funds.

T. C. MORRIS, Chairman.

---o---

THE CARMARTHENSHIRE INFIRMARY BUILDING COMMITTEE IN ACCOUNT WITH THE TREASURERS

PAYMENTS.	£	s.	d.	RECEIPTS.	£	s.	d.
To Site of Building	550	0	0	By Sundry Donations	2125	5	0
Conveyance and Drawing Contract ...	38	5	8	Interest on India Bonds, bought July, September, October, and November, 1855, sold in June, 1857	21	10	1
Mr. Collard for Plan	15	15	0	Collection and Admittance Tickets on the occasion of laying Foundation Stone, less expences	21	3	5
Paid Mr. Lewis, contractor, as per account.	3450	0	0	Dr. Lloyd, 2 years' Rent of Garden	6	0	0
Mr. Jenkins, architect, Commission and Travelling Expenses	256	0	0	£2,300 India Bonds, part of the Floating Capital of the Institution sold from time to time, as required, under the authority of a special meeting of the Subscribers ..	2335	8	6
Clerk of the Works	56	5	0	Balance carried forward	56	3	7
Mr. Geo. Goode, for valuation ...	5	5	0				
Mr. Johnson, for drawing Working Plans..	5	0	0				
Ventilators	3	12	11				
One year's Tithe Rent Charge, due January, 1858	0	7	0				
Mr. Rhys Jones, for Grates, Gas Fittings, Hanging Bells, Kitchen Range, &c., &c., as per bill	115	0	0				
Amount transferred to General Infirmary Account for furnishing House	70	0	0				
	£4,565	10	7		£4,565	10	7
To Balance brought forward	56	3	7				

JNO. MANSEL, Chairman.

7. Annual Report from 1st April, 1858 to 31st March, 1859 continued with Report of Building Committee.

HOUSE SURGEON'S REPORT

For the year ending March 31st, 1890.

GENTLEMEN,—The total number of patients that have received the benefits of the Institution during the year amounts to 916.

Of this number 754 were Out-patients and 162 In-patients.

OUT-PATIENTS—

Under treatment April 1st, 1889	155
Admitted during the year	599
Total	754

The result of treatment was as follows:—

Discharged cured	384
Relieved	261
Died	5
Remaining under treatment	104
Total	754

OUT-PATIENTS—

Recommended by Governors	396
Urgent cases	128
Accidents	75
Total	599

IN-PATIENTS—

Recommended by Governors	105
Urgent cases and accidents	57
Total	162

IN-PATIENTS—

Under treatment April 1st, 1889	24
Admitted during the year	138
Total	162

The result of treatment of In-patients:—

Cured	69
Relieved	70
Died	6
Remaining under treatment	17
Total	162

Average number of In-patients in the House throughout the years—

1889-90	21
1888-89	17·5
1887-88	15·5

Average cost of both In and Out-patients in medicine, instruments, and appliances, for the years—

	s. d.
1890	1 9½
1889	1 9¼
1888	1 3¾
1887	1 9¾

Average cost per week of each inmate, including Resident Staff, Nurses, and Servants, for diet, including wine, spirits, and beer for Patients, for the years—

	Per Week s. d.	Per Year £ s. d.
1889-90	6 2	16 0 8
1888-89	5 11½	15 9 10
1887-88	5 2¾	13 11 11

MEDICAL CASES.

Anæmia	Influenza
Arthritis	Ichthyosis of Tongue
Bright's Disease	Neuroasthenia
Bronchial Asthma	Neurosis
Bronchitis	Optic Neuritis
Cirrhosis of Liver	Peritonitis
Chorea	Pneumonia
Cerebro-spinal disseminated Schrosis	Pleurisy
Chlorosis	Pulmonary Phthisis
Diabetes	Paraplegia
Carcinoma of Liver	Rheumatism, Acute
Emphysema	,, Sub-acute
Empyema	,, Chronic
General Debility	Sciatica
Heart Disease	Struma
Hemiplegia	Tuberculosis, General
Hemichorea	Uræmia

8. House Surgeon's Annual Report for the year ending 31st March, 1890.

GYNECOLOGICAL CASES.

Pelvic Cellulitis	Rudimentary Uterus
Endo-cervicitis	Cervical Catarrh
Uterine-fibroid Tumour	Urethral Caruncle

The OPERATIONS were—

Tenotomy, for the relief of	... Tulipes Equino Varus
Plastic Operation ,,	... Hare Lip
Excision ,,	... Scirrhus of Breast
Excision ,,	... Enlarged Tonsil
Osteotomy ,,	... Caries of Bone
Amputation of Arm ,,	.. Compound Fracture
Amputation of Finger ,,	... Crushed Hand
Strangulation ,,	... Uterine Tumour
Excision ,,	... Epithelioma of Lip
Excision ,,	... Epithelioma of Ear
Operation for ...	... Strangulated Hernia

SURGICAL CASES.

Abscess in Arm	Disease of Knee Joint
,, Leg	,, Shoulder Joint
,, Thigh	Keratitis
,, Lumbar	Periostitis of Femur
,, Perinium	Periosteal Sarcoma of Femur
Abscess Psoas	Caries of Spine
,, Tubercular	,, Sterum
Carbuncle	,, Clavicle
Epithelioma of Ear	,, Lower Jaw
,, Lip	,, Phalnx
Hæmatocele	Growth Super. Maxillary Bone
Hare Lip	Genu Valgum
Hernia Ingrimal	Fistula in Ano
,, Femoral	Phlebitis
Iritis	Ophthalmia
Lupus of Nose	Orchitis
Lipoma	Ulcers Strumous
Psoriasis	,, Varicous
Disease of Hip Joint	

ACCIDENTS.

Compound Fracture of Skull, with Brain penetrating	Scald of Foot
Fractured Femur	,, Feet and Leg by hot vitriol
,, Clavicle	Dislocated Shoulder
,, Ribs	,, Elbow
,, Humerus	,, Ditto Compound
,, Ditto Compound	,, Thumb
,, Radus and Ulna	Crushed Foot
,, Ditto Compound	,, Hands
Ethmoid and Inf. Turbinated Bones	Contused and Lacerated Wound of Forearm

PARISHES AND DISTRICTS FROM WHICH PATIENTS WERE RECEIVED.

Abernant	Llandilo-fawr	Llanstephan
Abergwili	Llanboidy	Mydrim
Carmarthen	Llangendeirne	Mynyddygarreg
Conwil	Llangathen	Newcastle-Emlyn
Drysllwyn	Llangain	Newchurch
Eglwysfair	Llangunnor	Pontyates
Germany	Llangadock	Pencader
Kidwelly	Llanfynydd	Pontyberem
Lampeter	Llanfihangel-Rhosycorn	Trelech
Llandovery	Llanllawddog	Tenby
Llanarthney	Llansawel	St. Clears
Llandyssil	Llanybri	
Llandefeilog	Llanwinio	

COMPARATIVE STATEMENT.

	1886	1887	1888	1889	1890
In-patients ...	122	119	106	147	162
Out-patients ...	523	632	551	824	754
	645	751	657	971	916

I am, Gentlemen,

Yours respectfully,

J. T. CRESWICK WILLIAMS,

L.R.C.P. (Lond.), M.R.C.S. (Eng.), L.S.A. (Lond.)

9. House Surgeon's Annual Report (continued) for year ending 31st March, 1890.

10. Infirmary's Red Cross Detachment at Penlan Workhouse, 1915
Matron Linda Ditcham, 2nd row, 1st left.

11. Christmas on the Children's Ward probably 1915.

12. Dedication of War Memorial probably 1920.

GOVERNORS OF THE INFIRMARY are:—

1. Annual Subscribers of One Guinea and upwards.

2. Nominated Representatives of Congregations who make an annual collection of Three Guineas or upwards.

3. Donors of Ten Guineas and upwards.

4. Nominated Representatives of any association of persons who make a contribution of Three Guineas or upwards are Governors for One Year. If the contribution amounts to Twenty Guineas or upwards, the nominated representatives are Governors for life.

PRIVILEGES OF GOVERNORS.

Governors who subscribe annually One Guinea a year can recommend out-patients.

Governors who subscribe Two Guineas or upwards, and Representatives of Congregations or Associations, can recommend both out- and in-patients.

NOTICE.

Governors recommending Patients will please note that during the current Infirmary Year the Weekly Meeting of the House Committee will be held on Tuesdays, at 11 a.m.

Forms of Recommendation may be obtained from the Hon. Secretary, or the Matron at the Infirmary.

13. Governors' Nominating Privileges printed in Annual Report, 1890.

Carmarthenshire Infirmary.

NURSES FOR THE SICK IN PRIVATE FAMILIES

Can be supplied from the Institution

—— on application to ——

THE MATRON, The Infirmary, Carmarthen.

Tel. 60.

SCALE OF CHARGES:

Non-Contagious Cases, per week	...	...	£2	10	0
Contagious Cases	”	...	3	3	0
Single Day or Night	...	...	0	7	6

Laundry Expenses—3/6 per week additional.

Travelling Expenses to and from a Patient to be paid by the Employer direct.

Ten Shillings a week extra is charged if Nurses sleep in the Infirmary.

OLD LINEN AND FLANNEL ARE MUCH NEEDED.

14. Private Nurses, Annual Report, 1900.

USE OF THE X-RAY APPARATUS.

N.B.—No Subscriber's Letter of Recommendation is necessary.

1.—The CHARGE FOR EXAMINATION depends upon the circumstances of the Patient and upon the size and Number of Plates required, and Varies from Half-a-crown to Two Guineas.

N.B.—The actual fee charged is decided by the Hon. Medical Officer at the time of Examination.

II.—Use of the Apparatus for Treatment.
For treatment of Cancer, Rodent Ulcer, Lupus, Ringworm, &c., the fees depend on the length of treatment, and are decided by the Hon. Medical Staff.

X-Ray Examination and X-Ray Treatment of in-patients or out-patients of the Infirmary are free of charge to the patient, if considered beneficial by the Hon. Medical Staff.

Nurses may be Examined and Treated at Reduced Fees.

On application, persons who are not patients of the Infirmary may benefit by X-Ray examination and treatment on payment of the required fee.

15. Diagnostic and therapeutic X-rays, 1920.

16. The Infirmary in the early 1920s with a “Sanitary” Wing on the left

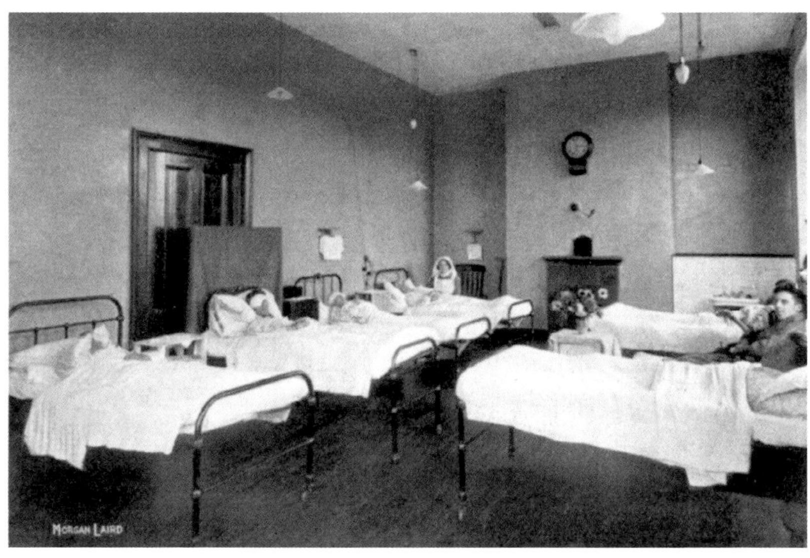

17. “Men’s” Ward, 1933.

18. Nurses' Sitting Room in the Nurses Hostel, 1933.

19. Nurses' Dining Room in the Nurses Hostel, 1933.

20. Rear view of Infirmary showing the balcony
with the Nurses Hostel on the left, 1933

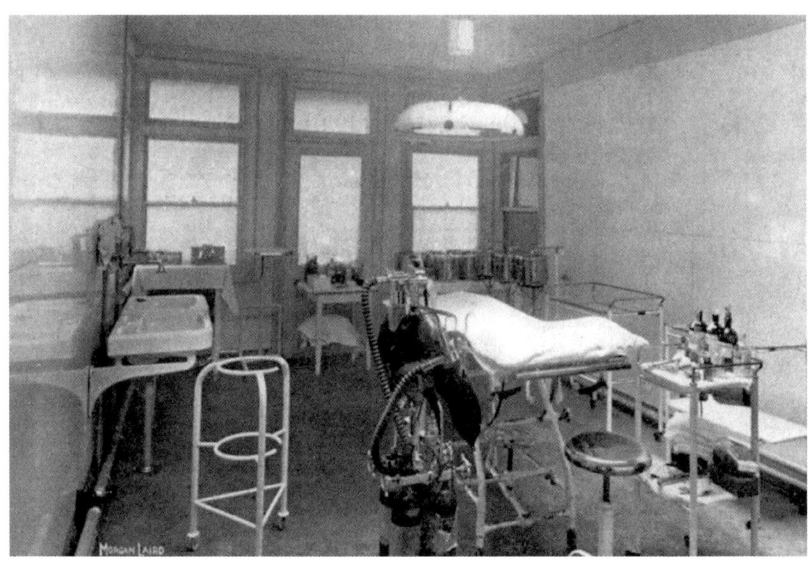

21. Infirmary Operating Theatre, 1933.

22. Carnival Brochure August, 1933 "Proceeds in aid of Proposed Maternity Ward."

23. Foundation Stone of "New" Wing and Lady Dynevor, 14th May, 1936.

24. Matron Dorothy Hartland and the entire Infirmary Nursing Staff in 1936 just prior to the major expansion of the institution in 1937.

25. The Duke and Duchess of Kent at Carmarthen Station, 19th October, 1937 prior to the opening of the "New" Wing by the Duchess.

26. Nursing and Domestic Staff awaiting the arrival of the Duke and Duchess of Kent in the forecourt of the Infirmary on the 19th October, 1937

27. Infirmary Management Committee and senior Nursing Staff, 19th October, 1937
Front row 1st from right Mr. J.R.E. James, County Obstetrician and
front row 2nd from right Dr. J.J. Healy, Consultant Ophthalmologist

28. Infirmary Housemaids, 1938.

29. Nurses Hostel and "New" Wing on the left taken from the balcony, 1938.

30. Rear of Nurses Hostel and "New" Wing on the right, 1938

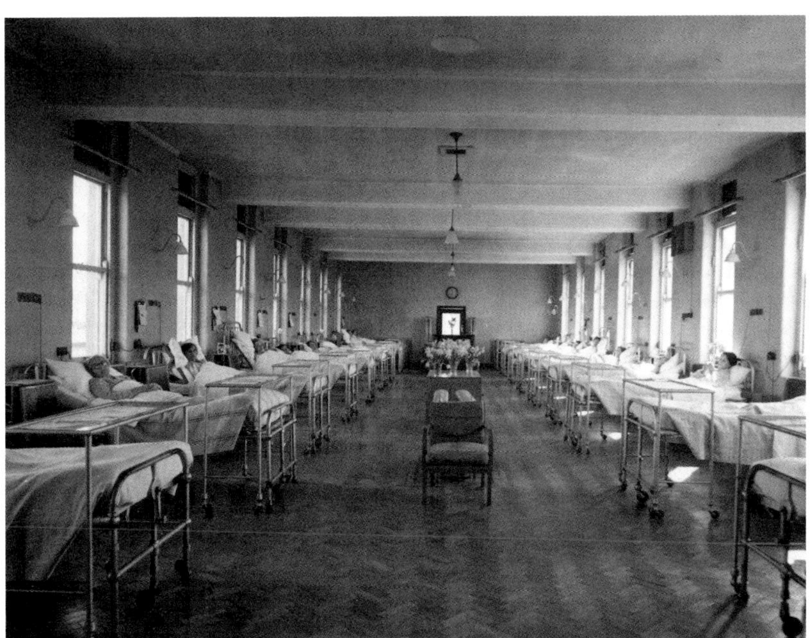

31. Female Surgical "Nightingale" Ward in the "New" Wing, 1938.

32. American Military Hospital, Glangwili, 1942
The hospital consisted entirely of Nissen Huts seen in the background.
The staff were accommodated in a separate camp of large tents and Nissen
Huts which are clearly seen in the foreground behind the houses on Dolgwili Road.

33. Accommodation tents for the staff of the American Military Hospital, 1942

34. Main American Military Hospital seen from above Dolgwili Road, 1942.

CHAPTER IV

PATIENTS, NURSES AND THE NURSING PROFESSION

No doubt the 11 patients who were transferred from the Gaol to the new Infirmary in Priory Street found their new surroundings much more congenial than the old. But a rigid system of discipline was imposed upon them by their upper-class benefactors who strongly disapproved of the modus-vivendi of the poor. No ambulant patient was to leave the Infirmary without the permission of his physician or surgeon possibly to prevent him returning drunk. Nevertheless, we read in the Minutes on the 6th October, 1858 that:

> *"Edward Richards got drunk and was abusive to the Matron and was immediately discharged."*[1]

It was stipulated that those of the patients who were able to work were to:

> *"...assist the Matron, nurse or other servant in nursing the patients, washing and ironing the linen, washing and cleaning the ward and in doing such other work as the Medical Officers and Matron may require."*[2]

It was required that:

> *"They do not swear or give abusive language or behave themselves indecently in any other way on pain of expulsion; they shall not be allowed to play at cards or dice or any other game or smoke in the wards."*[2]

No male patient was to go into the women's wards or women into the male wards. Whilst the Infirmary was still accommodated in the Borough Gaol, the House Committee actually appointed a sub-committee which they entitled "Committee for the Division of the

Men's from the Women's Wards." On the 23rd March, 1853 the sub-committee advised that it be effected by placing:

> *"An iron gate, now in a ward, across the upper passage; that the gate be kept locked; that the men use the yard to the south and the women that to the north; that the key of the division gate be kept by the House Surgeon or Matron and on no account be given to the patients."*[2]

It is not surprising that difficulties were experienced in this respect because the patients were not permitted any entertainment other than religious observances and were *"specifically forbidden to indulge in most of their customary recreations."*[3] These rules were strictly enforced until the Annual General Meeting in 1870 when the Rev. Latimer Jones, Vicar of St. Peter's, persuaded the meeting that no harm would come from allowing the patients to *"to play draughts and other innocent games in the Infirmary."*[1] Although the question of discipline caused lively and inconclusive discussions at Annual General Meetings it was generally held that:

> *"Discipline was essential to institutions of this nature which would otherwise become more like a bear garden than anything else."*[1]

When patients came to be drawn from a higher social class, as the benefits of hospital care came to be appreciated, the system was relaxed by non-enforcement of the rules rather than revocation.

Visiting time was between 9am and 4pm on Wednesday and Saturday only, market days, but each visitor had to obtain the permission of the Matron or House Surgeon before seeing his relative or friend. No major change was made until 1912 when new rules were drawn up and printed in English and Welsh to regulate visiting. Visiting time was to be between 2pm and 4pm, two visitors only to each patient and no visitor was to remain in the Infirmary for more than 30 minutes. Each visitor was enjoined to:

> *"Speak in low tones of voice, move quietly and remain at*

> *the bedside of the patient they visit. Visitors are not to bring food of any kind into the Infirmary."*[2]

In 1847 the Rules required the patients to:

> *"Retire to that part of the room where their bed is placed when members of the House Committee or the medical officers enter the ward. Any patients who do not conform exactly to the rules will incur the disgrace of being discharged for irregularity which would render them incapable of future admission to the benefits of this charity. However, should any of the patients not receive any of the comforts which it is the object of this charity to afford, or have any other cause to be dissatisfied they are requested to complain to the House Committee at its weekly meeting by whom they will be heard with attention or their grievances redirected if reasonable."*[2]

Patients were, perhaps, ill-advised to take advantage of this rule. An entry in the Minutes on the 1st November, 1849 records that:

> *"Whereas Thomas Andrews, an in-patient, preferred a complaint this day to the Committee that the food supplied to him on Sunday last was tainted; the Committee proceeded to investigate this complaint and are perfectly satisfied that there are no grounds whatever for it. The Committee have also found that Andrews' conduct is disorderly, that he swears and goes into the women's wards and the Committee have admonished him as to his future conduct and resolved that the House Surgeon expel him the House should he again so misconduct himself."*[1]

Each discharged patient was required to appear before the House Committee and asked his opinion of the care he had received. As a result the Minute Books contain a fairly well-balanced record of compliments and complaints. On the one hand we have a patient asserting that *"the Prince of Wales could not have received better treatment"* and on the other a female patient complained that the milk diet prescribed by her doctor "disagreed with her. In general the recorded opinions are both trivial and ill-informed and valueless as a source from which to draw conclusions.

Another rule ordered that:

> *"The number of patients discharged cured during the preceding month be delivered to the Vicar of Carmarthen, with a request that on the first Sunday of each month he return thanks for and on behalf of those who desire to do so."*[2]

The Committee further ruled that *"patients of other persuasions should, on their recovery, return thanks in their respective places of worship."*[2] This rule was revoked in 1875 when it was felt to be unscientific and undesirable that the care of the body should become confused with the care of the soul.

Although stern the Committee were often magnanimous in their attitude towards patients. Small sums of money were allocated to enable patients to *"recuperate at the seaside."* Indeed, a special fund was eventually set up for this purpose. Funeral expenses of *"friendless patients"* were found and on one occasion we find proceeds from the sale of *"pigwash"* being used to pay the rail fare of a patient to his home in Somerset.[1]

By the end of the nineteenth century attitudes had become much less uncompromising than previously. The first Christmas concert for the patients was organized by the Matron, Miss Macintyre, in 1888 and well-wishers were encouraged to bring or send gifts of books, toys, fruit, flowers and papers. Some newspaper proprietors, including the owner of the **Daily Telegraph**, provided free copies of each edition and, as late as 1927, we read of a local butcher making his contribution by:

> *"...providing for a long period liver and sweet bread for a case of pernicious anaemia."*[1]

The diet of the patients and staff consisted in the main of meat, bread and potatoes supplemented by liberal quantities of alcohol which was generally held to be of medicinal value. Many hospitals kept expenses down by allowing, indeed expecting, relatives and friends to bring in food. The medical staff in Carmarthen, however, was determined that unauthorized victuals and liquor should not interfere with the efficacy of their treatment. Rule 27 stated that:

> *"The appointment of the particular diet of the patients be referred to the respective Physician or Surgeon and that no other provisions or liquors be brought into the house on any pretence whatever."*[2]

Staff "diet tables" were also drawn up by the doctors who were well aware that nurses in other hospitals were continually being reported for drunkenness, pilfering and extracting money from patients. Rule 29 provided that:

> *"Any officer or servant who shall give to or receive from, any tradesman, patient, servant or stranger any fee, reward or gratuity of any kind.....and any patient giving any fee, reward or gratuity shall be liable to instant dismissal; and the friends of the patients are desired not to give any money or make presents to any of the nurses or servants."*[2]

An abstract of weekly expenditure in June, 1851 reveals that the weekly average number of outpatients was 65 and inpatients 18.5. The weekly average expenditure per inpatient was 3s 9½d. This provided 4lbs 10½ozs of flour, 3lbs 3½ozs of meat and 6lbs 2ozs of potatoes per head per week. As the hospital was situated in a rural area milk, butter, eggs and fresh vegetables were easily obtainable and often freely given. On the 4th January, 1854 the Committee ordered the Matron to give the patients a light supper at 8pm *"under the direction of the House Surgeon."* Two weeks later it was decided that this was an unnecessary expense and dinner was fixed at 1.30pm and tea at 6pm. Christmas was celebrated in the traditional way.[1] On the 18th December, 1850 the Minutes ordered that:

> *"Roast beef and plum pudding be provided on Christmas Day for the officers of the establishment and such patients as the medical men will allow."*[1]

Special meals were also provided by patriotic Committee men to mark significant public occasions such as Royal Weddings and Jubilees.

At the Annual General Meeting in 1871 the Rev. Latimer Jones angrily refuted a suggestion that the food was:

> *"...not much better than that supplied to the inmates of Her Majesty's Prisons. I am well aware that a great many people regard life in the Infirmary as Gaol life but nothing whatever is stinted and, indeed, the Chairman himself when ill did not receive better treatment than patients in the Infirmary. Eating and drinking of the best is freely given. Patients are supplied with port wine, milk, eggs and milk puddings, where necessary and they ought to understand that whilst in the Infirmary they live as gentlemen in their own residences."*[4]

Preserved material regarding the early years is scarce and the main source from 1846 to the early 1880s has been the Minute Books in the County Archives and the two weekly local newspapers, the **Carmarthen Journal** and the **Welshman**, with their reports of the Annual General Meetings. From 1888 the Annual Reports were published by the Infirmary and printed at the Welshman newspaper's premises in Lammas Street. It is disappointing that the House of Commons Enquiry "Hospitals of the United Kingdom" conducted by Dr. J.S. Bristowe, Senior Physician at St. Thomas's Hospital and Mr. T. Holmes Senior Surgeon at St. George's Hospital, in 1863, whilst reporting for the Privy Council on every voluntary hospital in England, Scotland and Ireland includes not a single reference to institutions in Wales.

Advertisements in the **Carmarthen Journal** and **Welshman** in the 1850s stipulated that nurses should be *"not under 30 years of age and conversant with the Welsh language"*. The salary was to be £14 per annum with board and lodging provided. The porter was required to be *"over 30 and under 50 years of age and an old soldier is preferred".*

It is uncertain exactly what hours the nurses and servants were expected to work for their meagre wages at that time. They would certainly have been extremely long and "days off" unknown. Holidays were only granted in exceptional circumstances and application had to be made to the Committee. The records are also vague about the arrangements made at night although on the 21st January, 1855 we read that the Secretary was ordered:

> *"...to pay 1s. 6d. to the man sitting up with Henry Bishop."*[1]

In 1847, The London Hospital was obliged to appoint a Committee to investigate a number of cases of serious illness amongst their nursing staff. It reported that:

> *"The general disorder of the health of the nurses is brought on from excessive fatigue induced by having to perform both day and night duty with but a short and hurried interval of rest between these periods of attendance in the wards."*[3]

That a similar system existed in Carmarthen is evidenced by a laconic entry in the Minutes on the 2nd February, 1859:

> *"The nurse asked to be excused sitting up at night on account of her bad health – granted."*[1]

The following week an additional female servant was engaged presumably to be available to *"sit up at night."*

The Rules and Regulations enjoined the nurses and servants to be:

> *"...diligent and attentive to the wants of the patients and to shew neither partiality nor ill-will to any of them."*[2]

They were to:

"Clean their respective wards before 7am in the summer and 8am in the winter and allow no foul linen or bed clothes to be kept or remain on the wards but to take them immediately to the Matron who will cause them to be carried to the washhouse........and to scour their respective wards with soap and warm water or lees every Friday morning before 7.30am in summer and 8.30am in winter."[2]

The time schedule was presumably arranged to save the expense of artificial lighting. They were to:

"Adopt every means in their power to promote cleanliness in the person of the patients and ventilation in the wards and punctually administer the medicines according to the directions and carry without delay the phials, gallipots etc. to the Dispensary....they are not to leave the house without permission from the Matron and any nurse or any servant disobeying any order they may receive from their superiors, or neglecting any of their duties shall be immediately discharged and considered incapable of again being received into the service of the Infirmary."[2]

In the early years the Matron was a subordinate official, in fact, little more than domestic supervisor and housekeeper. It was laid down that she should be:

"...unmarried and without the care of a family."[2]

The age requirement was changed at the first Annual General Meeting from between 35 and 50 to between 30 and 60 so that Mrs Rowlands could be employed. It was ordered that:

"She shall keep an inventory of the Household goods and furniture and be responsible for the same, she shall weigh and measure the provisions brought into the house and keep an account thereof and she shall receive no article whatever unless accompanied by a bill of parcels, with the

> *price affixed thereto, to which she must put her initials if correct and deliver to the secretary with her weekly account; she shall visit the wards in the morning, at dinner time and in the evening and shall see that the wards and other apartments, together with the beds, clothes and linens etc. are kept neat and clean and that no sand be used."*[2]

She had to:

> *"...consult with the Secretary and House Surgeon about the purchase of provisions and other necessaries and attend to their distribution according to the diet table which shall be given to her by the House Surgeon."*[2]

She was required to:

> *"Superintend the conduct of the patients, nurses and servants and take care that the Rules relating to their conduct be read over to them every Saturday; she shall report all cases of misbehaviour to the House Committee; she shall keep the keys of the House and see that the doors are closed at 9 o'clock in the evening and opened at 7 o'clock in the morning unless otherwise ordered by the House Committee."*[2]

Matron was permitted to employ a washerwoman when needed and she arranged for a barber to visit twice per week to shave patients for which he was paid 3 shillings. There were disciplinary problems and, for example, in April, 1849 it is recorded that a nurse was immediately discharged the Matron having *"made a complaint against her for disobedience"*. She was, however, allowed a month's wages in lieu of notice.

Countless books have been written about the nursing reform movement which started in the second half of the nineteenth century. Most historians are unanimous in condemning the old untrained nurses and romanticizing the "lady nurses" trained at the School set up by

Florence Nightingale at St. Thomas's Hospital in 1860. 'Lady' pupil nurses had attended King's College Hospital from 1856 so it was not the first of its kind in the United Kingdom. Miss Nightingale, herself, had had only minimal training in Alexandria, Egypt, at a religious establishment in Kaiserswerth, Germany and in Paris. However, as Professor Abel-Smith points out, it is not unusual for reformers to overstate the evils they are trying to remedy. He quotes one of Miss Nightingale's favourite pupils, Miss Pringle, who wrote after 12 years practical experience:

> *"Some of the nurses were the best type of woman – clever, dutiful, cheerful and kind, endowed above all with that motherliness of nature which is the best attribute of a nurse."*[3,5]

The sisters at St. Bartholomew's Hospital had, in 1830:

> *"...an admirable sagacity and a sort of rough practical knowledge which was nearly as good as any acquired skill."*[3,5]

But nursing was little more than a specialized form of charring – many tasks, which these days are carried out by nurses, were performed by the House Surgeon or his apprentices. The major vice attributed to the untrained nurse was drink. Certainly, the nurses and servants were given alcoholic drinks as rewards for carrying out repulsive or disagreeable tasks. On the 24th April, 1848 we read in the Infirmary Minutes that 2s. per week was allowed for beer for servants of the establishment and this expenditure became a regular feature of the monthly statement of accounts.[1]

The standard of nursing in the early nineteenth century, says Professor Abel-Smith, was what each hospital chose to make it. If the accommodation and conditions of work were such that decent women would undertake the work, decent women offered their services. Where nurses were carefully selected by the Matron and sufficiently controlled by the medical staff their standard was high. But where the hospital authorities did not make proper arrangements the standard of nursing was extremely low.[3,5] He quotes **The Times** who summarized the position in 1857:

> *"Hospital nurses have been much abused – they have their faults but most of them are due to want of proper treatment. Lectured by committees, preached at by chaplains, scowled on by treasurers and stewards, scolded by Matrons, sworn at by surgeons, bullied by dressers, grumbled at and abused by patients, insulted if old and ill-favoured, talked to flippantly if middle-aged and good-humoured, tempted and seduced if young and well-looking, they are what any woman might be under these circumstances."*[3,5]

The Matron, Mrs. Elizabeth Rowlands, was replaced by Mrs. Sarah Thomas in 1851 who, in turn, was succeeded by Mrs. Catherine Bevan in 1865. The 1871 Census reveals that, on census night the Infirmary accommodated 25 inpatients including 3 children aged 1, 4 and 8 years. The remainder were in their teens, twenties and thirties. The resident staff were Charles Bridgstock, 29, House Surgeon; Catherine Bevan, 49, Matron; Sarah Harries, 24, Nurse; Hannah Jones, 29, Cook; Elizabeth Jones, 20, Housemaid; Jane Jones, 21, Housemaid and John Thomas, 26, Porter. All were unmarried except Mrs. Bevan who was a widow.

It was not until 1885 that the House Committee finally decided to advertise for a trained Matron and even then the principal motive was to increase the income of the Infirmary. At the Annual General Meeting in April the decision was announced that:

> *"Upon the resignation of Mrs. Bevan, the late Matron, an opportunity presented itself for further increasing the utility of the Infirmary and it was resolved that the new Matron should be a trained and certificated nurse of experience, who should be able to properly teach and train nurses, so that if occasion should arise their services might be available in the sick houses of those for whom the Infirmary was not primarily intended."*[6]

The Committee, therefore, proposed to have probationers, preferably aged 25 years or over, and announced that the first had just been employed. It was regretted that the falling-off in amounts from subscriptions still continued but:

> *"In view of the determination of the Committee to increase the usefulness of the Infirmary by training nurses whose services might be of immense advantage in private houses the Committee appeal with confidence to the public to support it in this endeavour."*[6]

The first *"trained and certificated"* Matron, appointed in 1885, was Miss Reeve (highly recommended by Miss Victoria Jones, Matron of Guy's Hospital) who died shortly after taking up the post. In 1886 Matron was paid £41. 19s. 6d. per annum. The House Surgeon received £116 15s. 0d., Sister £19 19s. 0d., Junior Nurse £16 1s. 6d. and a Probationer £11 18s. 11d.

Then a Miss Lambert was appointed only to resign to *"take up a more lucrative appointment"* followed by a Miss Macintyre in 1888. A Miss Rimington was appointed in 1890 and supervised 3 probationers. Initially, probationer training was of an informal nature consisting mainly of bedside teaching by the Matron and House Surgeon. In 1892 the Committee decided that the number of probationers should increase to 4 and they would receive formal instruction in:

> *"...all branches connected with the art of nursing and certificates of competence will be awarded after certain examinations have been successfully passed."*[6]

A sister was also added to the establishment at this time. Uniforms for nurses were introduced in 1896. Then we read in the Minutes that a skeleton had been purchased for 9 guineas in 1899, *"for the doctors to teach the nurses"* and it was ordered that it be kept in a locked wooden cabinet. The following year an *"anatomical model"* was purchased.[6]

Miss Rimington was replaced by Miss Harries of St. Clears in 1892 who resigned in 1898 and was followed by Miss Linda Ditcham. Miss

Ditcham had trained at St. Bartholomew's Hospital, London under the formidable Matron, Miss Ethel Gordon Mason who married a Bart's physician and as Mrs. Bedford Fenwick began a campaign, by founding the British Nurses Association in 1887 and then the British College of Nursing, to procure a nationally recognized certificate for nursing and to advocate the establishment of a General Nursing Council to regulate the profession. Florence Nightingale and most doctors, however, were against the "professionalisation" of nursing through registration.

We read in the Annual Report for 1901 that:

> *"the training scheme for nurses which was initiated by the present Matron (Miss Ditcham) has now been fairly tested and may be said to be successful."*[6]

It evolved into a 4 year course; 2½ years at the Infirmary, 6 months in a London Hospital and 1 year on the "Out-Nursing" staff.

The College of Nursing, founded in 1916, sought a Royal Charter and wanted to become the sole authority for granting certificates to trained nurses. It was implacably opposed by the British Nurses Association and Mrs. Bedford Fenwick who wanted nurses to be registered by the State. Both organizations were, later, to add the prefix 'Royal'. The House Committee of the Infirmary were much annoyed that the College was refusing to admit nurses who had trained in hospitals with less than 50 beds stating as its reason that:

> *"...nurses trained in smaller hospitals are a danger to the public."*[6]

In 1920 the House Committee informed subscribers that:

> *"The absurdity of such a rule, and the folly of such a statement are evident when it is known that the Matrons and Sisters, in our larger hospitals engaged in the training of nurses, were themselves trained in hospitals of less than 50 beds. Such Matrons and Sisters would be 'a danger to*

> *the community' whilst those they have trained, or are training, would be admitted certificated members to the College of Nursing! Your Committee wrote a strong protest against both the rule and the statement having ample evidence that for ability, conduct and devotion the nurses trained at Carmarthen are not a whit inferior to those trained in our largest hospitals."*[6]

The Government intervened and the Nurses Act of 1919 set up the General Nursing Council and Mrs. Bedford Fenwick became the first name on the world's first Nursing Register. The Royal British Nurses Association won this particular battle but the Royal College of Nursing went on to become the pre-eminent professional association for nurses. It is not until 1929 that we read in the Annual Report that the House Committee had had to concede that the Infirmary was too small to provide a full training for nurses; nevertheless it was:

> *"...proud of the fact that the General Nursing Council for England and Wales have granted recognition to this Infirmary as a Hospital for training purposes. This recognition (which is provisional for two years commencing January, 1929) means that probationer nurses are now allowed to sit for their Preliminary State Examination after 2 years training here. Then, by favour of the Governing Body of Swansea General Hospital they proceed to Swansea for another 2 years where they sit for their final examination. If successful they become State Registered Nurses and may return to this Infirmary, as fully trained nurses, to serve in the wards or on the Private Nursing Staff."*[6]

Miss Ditcham remained in post for 28 years and during the First World War also served as Matron of the Red Cross Hospital of 60 beds established at the old Penlan Workhouse staffed by some of the Infirmary nurses and the Honorary physicians and surgeons to the Infirmary. Miss Ditcham's efforts were, clearly appreciated because we read in the Minute Book an entry dated the 15th April, 1918 that the Committee:

> *"...heartily congratulate Matron on the Honour (Royal Red Cross) conferred on her by His Majesty, the King."*[1]

She was affectionately remembered by Dr. James. J. Healy appointed as the first Consulting Ophthalmologist in 1921 and who later served as Chairman of the House Committee. We were fortunate to be able to interview Dr Healy, in retirement, at his home in April, 1967. Dr Healy said that Miss Ditcham was:

> *"A wonderful old lady, a Victorian type of Matron, kindly but starchy, a very forceful character and she had the complete confidence of the medical staff. She was always mistress of the situation and invariably had her way with the House Committee. She was a very professional woman then (1921), probably, about 60 years old. She was one of the old school who could meet people like Lady Dynevor on her own terms."*[7]

On only one occasion, the 12th May, 1911, do we read of any dispute between Miss Ditcham and the medical staff. The House Committee came down, firmly, on the side of the Resident Medical Officer of the time with regard to the: *"control of treatment"*. Interestingly, it was found impossible to recruit a House Surgeon in 1915 because all the young doctors had been called-up to serve in the Armed Forces. The Committee requested that:

> *"...the House Surgeon's duties be performed by the Matron."*[1]

This was such a satisfactory and economical arrangement, that it was allowed to continue until 1933 when the medical staff demanded *"as a result of a complaint"* that a Resident Medical Officer be recruited. In 1930, when the matter was raised it had been decided to employ a *"masseur"* (physiotherapist) instead of an R.M.O.[6]

We were also fortunate to be able to speak with Mrs. Laura Davies who had worked at the Infirmary for 31 years and had similar recollections of Miss Ditcham. Mrs. Davies spent 6 years as a Housemaid, 4 years as an Assistant Cook, 2 years in the Laundry, 1 year as Night Cook and 18 years on the telephone switchboard. She also recalled, with great affection, Matron Dorothy Hartland who would give up her bed for serious Maternity cases. She also used to cook and work in the Laundry when necessary. The staff felt sorry for her and everybody "mucked in" to help:

> *"Nobody was afraid of anybody in those days – we were just one big happy family and our whole lives revolved around the hospital."*[8]

Miss Ditcham had purchased a croquet set for the nurses and the House Committee raised money for a tennis court which was built in 1939 in the garden at the back of the hospital for the use of all the staff. In 1947 a caravan was purchased, and taken to Pendine Sands, where the staff could obtain *"much-needed rest at the seaside."* By then, the hours worked were shorter. Mrs. Davies recalled that the staff, both nursing and domestic, lived in the Infirmary until the Nurses' Hostel was built and opened in 1922 using surplus wartime Red Cross funds. Later several houses on The Parade (Nos. 1 to 5 – now demolished) were bought by the Infirmary and used for staff accommodation.[8]

There were open coal fires in each ward and one of Mrs. Davies's duties, as a 17 year old house maid, was to remove the ashes, clean the grates and fill the coal buckets. The fires were lit by the porter. Shifts for all staff were 6.30am to 9pm five days per week. 6.30am to 2pm one day per week and 6.30am to 6pm one day per week. On Sundays half the staff were sent off between 10am and 12.30pm to go to church and the other half from 2pm to 4.30pm. In the 1930s wages were still less than £2 per month but meals were provided. It was compulsory to wear uniform when going out on the one day per week that it was possible and all staff had to be back in the House by 8pm. Permission to go out had to be obtained from Matron who always grumbled, agreed, then said "don't ask me again". She often used to sit in her office, with a strategically placed mirror, to catch returning staff who had not obtained permission to leave the Infirmary! She also objected to the girls sitting on the wall by the new Wing talking to their boyfriends. The nurses wore grey "frocks" with aprons and caps in the summer and red in the winter – everybody changed on the same day.

Probationers' "frocks" were striped and domestic staff's dresses were plain blue.[8]

Lectures were given in the Committee Room and, later in Bethania Chapel Vestry just over the road, and fitted in when convenient. C. P. Parry, M.D. gave the lectures in General Medicine and J. Lloyd Davies, M.R.C.P., F.R.C.S. the Gynaecology lectures. Mr W.F. Brook, F.R.C.S. came from Swansea at least once a week and lectured in General Surgery. He was very popular with the patients and the Swansea train was held for him at Carmarthen Station if he was delayed. Prayers were held every night in the wards at 7pm and the nurses were expected to attend. Matrons Ditcham and Hartland used to say goodnight to each member of staff in their bedrooms. There were two Sisters in post in the 1920s and 1930s. Sister Jeremy was in charge of the wards and Sister Powell supervised Theatre, X-Ray, Outpatients and Casualty. There were no regular operating days and Sister Powell covered the Theatre both day and night. Sister Powell left in 1931 or 1932 and was replaced by Sister Edwards. When the new Wing opened in 1937 Nurse Gracie Hughes was promoted Sister and Sister Edwards became Assistant Matron as requested by the Honorary Medical Staff in a letter to the House Committee dated the 5th July, 1933. Sister Goodfellow was the first senior nurse to take charge of the new Wing. At that time, 1933, there were 3 sisters, 3 staff nurses and 8 probationers in post. Prior to 1937 there were usually 2 nurses on at night caring for perhaps 20 to 25 patients. As well as delivering direct patient care the nursing staff were required to answer the telephone in the Front Hall, prepare dressings and bandages and sterilise instruments by boiling. The Infirmary was much busier after the extension opened in 1937.[8]

Patients were mainly surgical, casualty, ENT and eyes. There were very few Maternity cases, before 1937, except the most seriously ill. The stairs on the left of the hall were used to carry up patients and by ambulant patients, nurses, domestic staff and visitors. The stairs on the right were known as the "Golden Stairs" and were for the exclusive use of the Physicians and Surgeons, members of the House Committee and Matron! A lift for patients was not installed until 1929 when the money was raised for one by the "Mayor's Infirmary Ball Committee".

The original lifts were used for food and a whistle was blown to attract attention from above. The ward maid used to ride down on these old lifts.[8]

There was a very formal relationship between the medical and the nursing staff in the 1920s and 1930s and Margaret Fox, Sister Tutor at The London Hospital, included guidelines in her "First Steps in Nursing "published in 1924:

> *"Take for instance the rules concerning the etiquette to be observed by the nurses in the ward towards members of the medical staff. They may not sit down, talk or move about unnecessarily, make any noise or allow the patients to do so while he is present. They must not address him unless he speaks first to them and then only as "Sir", never as "Mr. So and So". If directly asked a question they may answer but must never express an opinion of a patient's condition unless desired to do so. They must open and close the door for the doctor in-coming and out-going, see that he has water to wash his hands and wait on him quietly and unobtrusively. The same etiquette, slightly modified, is also required towards resident medical officers and all grades of medical students. This seems very strange and even ridiculous to some newcomers being a complete upheaval of all preconceived notions respecting the relations between modern man and woman The daughter of a duke, if she became a probationer, has to treat the surgeon, even though he should be the son of the local pork butcher, with the same deference for the reason that in hospital her relations towards him are not social but professional. He is her "Superior Officer" and must be recognized as such."*[9]

Miss Ditcham died, in harness, on the 5th June, 1926 and her portrait, which was hung in the Committee Room after her death is now at the West Wales General Hospital. The House Committee paid for her memorial stone in Carmarthen Cemetery. A Memorial Tablet placed in the Infirmary was unveiled by Lady Dynevor in 1928 and is now on display at the West Wales General Hospital. The new Matron, Miss Dorothy Hartland, was selected out of 29 applicants and was a State

Registered Nurse, a Member of the College of Nursing and held the Central Midwives Board Certificate. Miss Hartland served the Infirmary, for 22 years until she retired in 1948 and was replaced by Miss E. Miles, S.R.N., S.C.M. followed by Miss A. Sim, S.R.N., S.C.M. in 1955, Miss C.B.M. John, S.R.N., S.C.M. in 1957 and Miss A. Vaughan-Jones, S.R.N., S.C.M., R.F.N, 1961 to 1974.

A superannuation scheme for the nursing staff was introduced in 1932 following the report of the Lancet Committee on Nursing. Under the terms of the scheme the nurse paid one-third of the premium and the Infirmary two-thirds. At retirement, the beneficiary received either a lump sum or an annuity depending on the number of contributions. The House Committee commented:

> *"Our participation in this scheme will, of course, add to our expenditure, but the House Committee gladly undertakes the responsibility in the interests of one of the noblest of professions which, as admitted regretfully by everybody, is too inadequately paid to enable its members to make proper provision for old age."*[6]

Towards the end of 1940 a representative of the General Nursing Council made an official visit of inspection of the Infirmary which, by this time, had expanded to 105 beds. The outcome was that the Management Committee, as they were now entitled, were required to appoint a Sister-Tutor, Sister Capper-Williams, in order to become fully qualified as a complete training school for nurses. The affiliation with Swansea had continued to this date but, in early 1941, the General Nursing Council officially informed the Management Committee that the Infirmary had been recognized as a complete training school for general nurses. However, until 1954, preliminary State examinations continued to be taken at St Thomas Hospital, Haverfordwest and Finals at Parc Beck Nurses Training School in Swansea. In 1942 the Ministry of Health had requested that the hospital provide intensive 2 week courses, in general nursing, for auxiliary nurses to enable them to act as assistants to trained nurses working for the wartime Emergency Medical Service. In 1943, the Nurses Act granted legal status to these nurses and established a "roll" and a system of examination, admission and removal of names. They came to be called State Enrolled Nurses or SENs. At the Annual General Meeting in March 1947 it was announced that it had been decided to:

> *"...augment the female nursing staff with male nurses and the first appointments have already been made."*[6]

Conditions at the old Infirmary and the hutted Glangwili site of the old American Military Hospital (see Chapter VII) which had been acquired from the War Office in 1947, of course, remained primitive. In 1954, a new General Theatre in a purpose-built brick building had been provided at Glangwili. Another General Theatre and the ENT Theatre were accommodated in Nissen huts. Instruments were sterilised by boiling and dressings autoclaved at the Infirmary. There was no Recovery Room so patients were taken back to the wards with a Guedel airway in place and recovered by the ward staff. By 1956, in addition to the Operating Theatres, there were three wards at Glangwili with 32 beds each, a Physiotherapy Department, Pathological Laboratory, School of Nursing, Chest Clinic and X-ray Department all accommodated in Nissen huts.

Construction of a new hospital had commenced in 1956 (see chapter VII) and in 1958, the new Ward Block 1 opened with three wards Teifi, Towy and Cleddau each with 32 beds. The first of two new Nurses' Homes with 100 rooms was also opened at this time. In 1961, Ward Block 2 opened with Ceri, Merlin and Preseli also with 32 beds each. The beds on Teifi (Sister Betty Evans) and Towy (Sisters Sadie Morris and Helen Rogers) were allocated to General Medicine. Cleddau (Sister Jeremy and Sister Pugh) was a paediatric ward. Ceri (Sister Pearl Davies) was entirely Orthopaedic. Merlin (Sister Mary Jones) and Preseli (Sister Iona Davies) accommodated General Surgery, Ophthalmic Surgery and ENT. The geriatric ward (Sister Petra Eplett) remained in a Nissen hut as did the School of Nursing and nursing administration. In 1960, the new Accident and Emergency Department (Sister Audrey Pullen) replaced the old Casualty Department in Priory Street Hospital which had been refurbished in 1952. Sisters Goodfellow and Emanuel remained the senior Sisters in Priory Street and the Theatre Superintendent for both hospitals was Sister Dulcie

Thomas, garrulous, amusing and enormously capable. The Operating Theatres at Glangwili were attached to the new blocks by means of long, temporary corridors and were eventually demolished. In 1963 the second Nurses' Home opened with 70 rooms. The ground floors of both Nurses' Homes now accommodate offices and departments.

In August, 1968, Ward Block 3, Cilgerran, Picton and Dynevor again with 32 beds each opened for patients. This enabled the obstetrics and gynaecology unit (Miles Phillips Wing) with the surgical wards in Priory Street Hospital to close in early 1969. Paediatrics was transferred from Cleddau, on the top floor of Ward Block 1, to Cilgerran on the ground floor of Ward Block 3 because, sadly, a child had fallen from a top-floor window. Dynevor (Sisters Goodfellow, and Dulcie Davies) became the Maternity Ward and Picton (Sister Marie Evans) was allocated to gynaecology.

Ward Block 4 was the last to open in December 1968. The ground floor contained an occupational therapy department and the Psychiatric Day Centre. Teilo (Superintendent, Miss Morgan) was allocated to psychiatric inpatients. Dewi Ward (Sister Petra Eplett) became the geriatric ward. On the third floor Padarn Ward (Sister Thelma Griffiths) had 20 "Chest" beds and 20 beds for infectious diseases. There were 4 cots allocated to Paediatrics and Dr. Keay, Consultant Paediatrician, was quick to transfer any child from Cilgerran who vomited or had diarrhoea in order to retain his beds.

The ward and departmental sisters were immensely experienced and were actively involved in teaching student nurses as well as advising, guiding and "disciplining" junior doctors. Most hospital doctors are more than happy to acknowledge the debt that they owe to experienced sisters and staff nurses particularly to those working in special care units such as neonatal, coronary, cardiac, surgical, medical and burns intensive care units.

Matron Vaughan-Jones kept a vigilant eye on all aspects of hospital activity including catering, housekeeping and laundering. These latter functions are now often "contracted-out" with, it is believed, some deterioration in standards. Matron's weekly rounds throughout both hospitals were grand affairs and, as a consequence, the wards were spotless and nursing care was provided to a very high standard. Although appropriately formal and dignified in manner Miss Vaughan-Jones took a personal interest in all her staff and their careers. Her wise counsel was usually heeded. There was also a "Home" Sister, Miss Roberts, who kept a benevolent eye on the new Nurses Home but some nurses still lived in the Nissen huts and were more difficult to supervise! There was a disciplined structure but the underlying tone, set by the Matron, was of good manners, kindliness and support. The lives of both senior and junior nursing staff revolved around the hospital just as Mrs. Davies remembered at the Infirmary in the 1920s and 1930s. Nurses wore a smart uniform and were highly respected both inside and outside the hospital. Nowadays, with the adoption by most hospitals of polo shirts or American-style trouser and "scrub" suits nurses are more difficult to identify and often seem scruffy.[10]

In 1952, the School of Nursing had been transferred to the Nissen huts at Glangwili and moved into its purpose-built accommodation in the new core block at the West Wales General Hospital in the summer of 1968. The Senior Sister Tutor, Miss Walters, was tall, elegant, witty and a fine teacher who was liked and respected by all who came into contact with her. Her assistant, Miss Squiers, had an encyclopaedic knowledge and was an excellent hands-on teacher. In 1967 the Central Midwives Board had been asked to approve the West Wales General Hospital for obstetric training which it supported subject to the appointment of an Obstetric Nurse Teacher. In fact, training did not begin until 1972 when a Senior Nursing Officer in Midwifery was appointed.[6]

The School of Nursing remained under Matron's control and student nurses learned by means of an apprenticeship supplemented by periods of classroom teaching and, moreover, were a crucial part of the hospital labour force. Standards were high and each year a Nurses' Prize-giving & Reunion was held when Gold, Silver and Bronze medals were distributed to the top 3 candidates in the State Final Examination and prizes of nursing textbooks awarded to the best students in each year of training and former students welcomed. The Chairman of the Management Committee and some of his colleagues, with representatives of the medical staff, attended and an eminent guest speaker addressed the gatherings and presented the prizes. A Christmas Concert was put on every year organised, principally, by the nursing staff who also published a weekly Hospital Newsletter. Until the opening of the Nurses' Recreation Room, now called the Cambrian Room, at Glangwili in 1958 concerts were given at the far end of the Nightingale female surgical ward in Priory Street.

In 1969 the General Nursing Council introduced a revised syllabus for the training of State Registered Nurses including, for the first time, a period in community care. Nurses were seconded to the Health and Social Welfare Department of the Carmarthenshire County Council.[6] District Nursing, in fact, dates back to 1863 but training was not well organised and local authorities could employ women without qualifications. Some looked to the Queen's Institute of District Nursing founded in 1887 to supply personnel others provided their own. Midwifery remained separate from nursing and the Community Midwife could always be relied upon to turn up on her bicycle or in her Morris Minor, day or night, when needed. Health Visitors were usually State Registered Nurses who had had further education and midwifery experience. Their roots lay in the nineteenth century when educated women became involved in social issues such as poverty, slums, infant mortality and appalling working conditions for women and children and they tended to embrace radical politics.[10]

The Salmon Report on nursing administration had been published in 1966 and its proposals were implemented in July 1970. Its aims were to place nurses in a proper management structure; to establish career development programmes for nurses with ability and potential and to help senior nurses retain clinical contact with patients. A hierarchical structure, graded by numbers, was introduced resulting in the effective abolition of the historic and honourable titles of Matron and Ward Sister. The Matron, Miss Vaughan-Jones, was appointed Group Chief Nursing Officer, Grade 10 supported by two Principal Nursing Officers (General and Psychiatric), Grade 9; and a bevy of Senior Nursing Officers at Grade 8 which included the former Sister Tutors. Ward Sisters languished at Grade 6 with few promotion prospects except into administration. Indeed, the doctors complained that the most highly trained clinical nurses were being promoted away from patients and into management.

In 1970, Professor Asa Briggs, a historian, was asked to review the roles, education and training of nurses and midwives because of the difficulties in recruitment, high wastage and the persistent demands by the Royal College of Nursing to end the dependence of hospitals on student nurse labour. The Report ignored its remit to look at the role of nurses and recommended that training should consist of two 18 month modules relating theory to practice in the clinical areas of medicine, surgery, psychiatry and the community. It proposed fewer but larger Colleges of Nursing, undergraduate degree courses and the creation of a unified statutory body for nursing and midwifery. In fact, it was NHS Reorganisation in 1974 that halved the number of nursing schools to 200.[10]

The Minister of Health, Barbara Castle, accepted the main findings of the Briggs Report in 1974 but it was 7 years before the statutory framework was set up and the United Kingdom Central Council for Nursing, Midwifery and Health Visiting (UKCC) finally came into being in April, 1983. It was replaced on the 1st April, 2002 by the Nursing and Midwifery Council (NMC). The NMC's principal functions are to maintain a register, to set standards for education, practice and conduct and to advise nurses, midwives and health visitors. It considers allegations of misconduct or unfitness to practise due to ill-health. The NMC also lays down post registration, education and practice (PREP) requirements. These are to complete a notification of practice form every three years and to undertake a minimum of 5 days continuing education. A personal professional profile containing details of professional development must be maintained. In 2004 the fee for triennial renewal of registration was £129.

The East Dyfed Health Authority was formed in April, 1982 and took over responsibility for the West Wales General Hospital, St. David's Hospital, Prince Philip Hospital, Llanelli and Bronglais Hospital, Aberystwyth. On the basis of the Briggs Report, the Schools of Nursing at these institutions were amalgamated and relocated in the Dyfed Nursing Block at Trinity College, Carmarthen, opened in 1983, but continued to be financed and managed by the Authority. Until this time nurses had tended to be loyal to the hospital in which they had trained and most wore their "hospital badges" with pride. Belts and buckles were also a mark of a nurses' status but are now discouraged by hospitals on grounds of infection risk!

In the 1980s nurse educationalists and the leaders of the profession began to look for autonomy and a role less dependent on doctors and the diagnosis and treatment of the acutely ill. They were outraged by their perception of the oppressed nurse as the doctor's handmaiden. Remarkably, this was at a time when women began to outnumber men at medical schools. Radical nurses, midwives and health visitors met informally and, occasionally held conferences. Their efforts culminated in Project 2000, accepted by the government in May, 1988, which moved nurse education to an academic and theory based model.[10]

Implementation of Project 2000 began in 1989 and provided that there should be a single level of registered nurse holding a Diploma or Degree in Nursing which meant that SENs were to be phased out. There would be a more advanced specialist grade such as health visiting and district nursing. A "support worker", which means a nursing auxiliary, would be employed to carry out duties which do not require a trained nurse. There was to be a common foundation course of 18 months followed by a second 18 months in a programme such as adult, child, mentally ill or mentally handicapped. Significantly, nursing was to be re-orientated towards the community. Schools of Nursing would link with higher education and students would have supernumerary status in hospitals whenever their training took them to one. There would be training grants and academic recognition of professional qualifications. Midwifery courses also became university-based.[10]

In January, 1992 the three Schools of Nursing managed by West Glamorgan, East Dyfed and Powys Health Authorities were amalgamated to form the Department of Nursing, Midwifery and Health Care, University of Wales, Swansea. In 1997 this Department was merged with the Centre for Philosophy & Health Care, the Department of Medical Physics and the Institute of Health Care Management, Swansea plus the Centre for Health Informatics, Aberystwyth to form the School for Health Science, Faculty of Education and Health Studies, University of Wales, Swansea. The School's major administrative, teaching and research activities are based at the main university campus in Swansea. There are also substantial centres on the Morriston Hospital campus and the Trinity College campus in Carmarthen with "outreach" staff at Withybush Hospital, Haverfordwest and Bronglais Hospital, Aberystwyth. For entry to a Diploma in Nursing course 5 O-Levels were required including Mathematics, English or Welsh and a Science. A-Levels at grade BCC or CCC are required to undertake a Bachelor of Nursing degree.[11]

In September, 2004 the School for Health Science at the University of Wales, Swansea clearly stated its aim of achieving an "all-graduate" profession in South Wales by withdrawing the option to study for the Diploma in Nursing. Whether this is prudent remains to be seen. It may be that many able young people anxious to serve in the nursing profession will be unable to achieve the academic entry requirements for a degree. Recruitment may also be difficult because there are so many other attractive vocational degree courses on offer. The NHS, with 1.3 million employees, is still the fifth largest employer in the world after the Peoples Liberation Army of Communist China, 2.3 million; US Department of Defense, 2 million; Indian Railways, 1.5 million and Walmart, 1.5 million! Nurses, of course, have always formed its largest group of workers numbering 137,636 in 1948 and 645,580 in 2003 – almost half of all NHS employees. As is well-known, there is already a staffing crisis in the NHS which has been reduced to recruiting nurses in India, the Philippines and South Africa, many of whom are in transit to the United States where salaries are more competitive. These countries have their own shortages and need to retain their nurses thus there is widespread criticism of developed countries recruiting in the third world. It is a matter of concern that the United States, in spite of rejecting an "all-graduate" nursing profession, is still predicting a shortage of 1 million nurses over the next decade and is actively recruiting in the United Kingdom.

The old apprenticeship system pioneered by Florence Nightingale and Mrs. Bedford Fenwick has been disparaged by the new academic nurses despite the fact that medical undergraduates and postgraduates continue to be taught at the bedside by practising clinicians.[10] The "nursing process" sets out to separate nursing, entirely, from what academic nurses call the "medical model" of disease a concept not recognised by doctors who were accused of regarding patients as collections of symptoms and signs. Doctors were irritated by this allegation because they believe that their role is still as it was defined by Ambroise Paré (1510-1590) in 16th century France: *"to cure sometimes, to relieve often and to comfort always."*[10] Certainly, medical advances and the dramatic reduction in lengths of stay meant that the role of the hospital nurse had to change. Despite the educational emphasis on nursing outside the acute-care setting and its independence from medicine, there is still a group of nurses who enjoy the challenges of "hi-tech" medicine in all disciplines.[10] They work in partnership with their medical colleagues often substituting for them.[10] The perceived gap between nurses and doctors is being bridged by the long-delayed emergence, in the United Kingdom, of the nurse practitioner.

> *Within the profession there has been a view that nursing, an honourable and worthy job, needed academic status to give it respectability. This was partly the result of an uncritical acceptance of ideas developed within the different cultural context of North America for which they might have been appropriate.*
>
> *A fight for higher status and university affiliation was accompanied by disparagement of traditional values and systems of management, such as the hospital matron. Instead there are a myriad of new initiatives, patient focused care, nursing audit, shared care, named nurses and nursing development units. Nurses persuaded government to put in place Project 2000, and adopted new but untested philosophies at a time when the demands on their profession were altering radically...*
>
> *Patients are discharged so fast that there is often little chance for nurses to establish a relationship. Clinical observation is replaced by tests and monitoring equipment. Specialisation in medicine demands increased specialisation in nursing if the two professions are to work side by side.*

> *Many basic and technical nursing duties are now performed by others – health care assistants, relatives and technicians. But this was the moment at which nursing moved away from the practical and basic into psychological and sociological paths which do not fit easily with the work of hospitals, although better adapted to community care, health promotion and the management of chronic disease. Some of the territory vacated by nurses has been occupied by others"*[10]

This was Dr. Rivett's view in 1998 as he looked back over 50 years of the NHS but, in fairness, it is too early to make a judgment and an objective verdict on academic nursing and its place in NHS practice in the 21st century is still awaited.

References:

1 Minute Books, County Infirmary, Carmarthen, 1846 to 1942, Carmarthenshire Archives Service.

2 Rules & Regulations County Infirmary, Carmarthen, 1846, 1857 and subsequent revisions, Carmarthenshire Archives Service.

3 The Hospitals - 1800 to 1948. A Study in Social Administration in England & Wales. Brian Abel-Smith, 1964, Harvard University Press.

4 Carmarthen Journal, 1810 to date (Microfim) Carmarthen Reference Library.

5 A History of the Nursing Profession. Brian Abel-Smith, 1960, Harvard University Press.

6 Annual Reports, County Infirmary, Carmarthen, 1846 to 1942, Carmarthenshire Archives Service.

7 James J. Healy, M.B. M.Ch., Consulting Ophthalmologist to the County Infirmary, Carmarthen 1921 to 1948 and to the West Wales General Hospital, 1948 to 1957. Chairman of the Management Committee, County Infirmary, Carmarthen, 1st January, 1946 to 5th July 1948. Personal communication, 28th April, 1967.

8 Mrs Laura Davies, Housemaid, Cook, Laundress and Telephonist at the County Infirmary and the West Wales General Hospital, Carmarthen, 1926 to 1969. Personal communication, April, 1967.

9 First Steps in Nursing 2nd Edition, Margaret E. Fox, 1924, Scientific Press, London.

10 From Cradle to Grave. Fifty Years of the NHS, Geoffrey Rivett, 1997, Kings Fund Publishing.

11 School of Health Science, University of Wales, Swansea. www.healthscience.swan.ac.uk

CHAPTER IV

MEDICAL STAFF AND THE MEDICAL PROFESSION

It should not be supposed that the duties of the Honorary Medical Staff were onerous – the brunt of the work was borne by the House Surgeon. Their work at the hospital formed only a small, non-essential and, of course, unpaid part of their practice. In time of war, however, things were rather different – most of the young doctors were called up leaving the older men to run the civilian hospitals. The fact that they had been elected to the Honorary staff attested to the confidence that the distinguished laymen who constituted the Governors placed in their abilities. Because of the very small number of Physicians living in the area of the Infirmary there was very little rivalry or jealously engendered. The results of any election to the staff would be a foregone conclusion because the local leaders of the profession would be well-known to the social elite who ran the Infirmary and in whose circles they moved. Eventually it became recognized that membership of any one of a small number of practices would result in an appointment at the Infirmary. Not only were the Honorary Medical Staff making their own personal contribution to the relief of the poor they were also retaining the goodwill of their patrons and, in addition, there was a good chance of becoming medical advisers to other subscribers.

Dr. Edmund Hills Stacey, (?c1790-1859), Mr. John Hughes, (1818-1897), Mr. John Rowlands, (1814-1899), Dr. Henry Lawrence (1784-1862), and Dr. John Bowen, were the members of the Honorary Medical Staff who, in 1847, wrote Rules to regularize their position and responsibilities and also the Rules which governed the institution throughout most of its existence. Apart from those which governed patient eligibility for treatment these Rules, subsequently, required little alteration. No person was eligible to be elected to the office of physician *"who is not, bona fide, a member of a British University or a Fellow of the Royal College of Physicians or otherwise legally and properly qualified."*[1] An Honorary Surgeon was to lay before the

Committee *"satisfactory proof"* that he was a member of the College of Surgeons of either London, Edinburgh or Dublin and a licensed Apothecary. The Medical Staff was to consist of two physicians and two surgeons and a Resident Surgeon/Apothecary. The medical cases belonged to the physicians and the surgical to the surgeons but it was left to the *"gentlemanly candour of both parties to call each other in to consult in cases requiring it."*[1]

Consultations with colleagues on all difficult or *"extraordinary"* surgical cases were to be held at:

> *"...one o'clock on Saturdays and oftener if necessary by the surgeon in attendance but either surgeon may request the attendance of the Physician in consultation upon his patient."*[1]

Every surgical consultation was to be:

> *"...regularly held in the consultation room and the result thereof entered by the surgeon whose patient is the subject of it in a book kept for the purpose and signed by all present."*[1]

If a disagreement arose the opinion of the majority was binding. *"should the number of votes be equal the physicians in the medical and the surgeons in the surgical shall decide the question."*[1] This is a remarkable adumbration of the Grand Round, Multidisciplinary Team aspect of the Quality Assurance/Clinical Governance programmes which were developed almost 150 years later. Unfortunately, all the old case books are missing, presumed destroyed, when on the 3rd June, 1918 Matron Ditcham was:

> *"...authorized to dispose of old books and papers that had accumulated at the Infirmary."*[2]

The Rules stated that:

> *"No capital operation shall be performed without a*

previous consultation for which the summonses shall be sent the day before except in cases of immediate necessity and then, if the operating surgeon have occasion for the assistance of the Physicians he shall direct that they be immediately summoned."[1]

Nobody was allowed to watch an operation:

> *"...without the consent of the faculty who are requested to make the Institution as available as possible to the profession by inviting their medical brethren to see the operations performed and the most interesting cases admitted into the Infirmary."* No post-mortem examinations were to be carried out *"unless the physician in the medical and surgeon in the surgical be present, the House Surgeon also being present during such examination; nor without the expressed consent of the relatives and friends of the deceased."*[1]

The Honorary Staff had to meet on the last Saturday of each month at 10 o'clock to *"consult the propriety of continuing their patients who have already been 2 months in the House."*[1] They were also to compile a Pharmacopoeia and diet regimen for patients and staff although on the 4th January, 1848 it was resolved that *"the Swansea diet table be adopted at the Carmarthen Infirmary."*[2] Once a month they had to visit the Dispensary with the House Surgeon to check the drugs and medicines and sign orders for fresh supplies. It was also considered necessary to remind each surgeon using instruments belonging to the Infirmary to:

> *"...cause them to be replaced, clean and in proper order in the repository."*[1]

The House Surgeon was specifically forbidden to practise outside the Infirmary in case he should take business away from the established practitioners. Initially, the rules stipulated that he was to contract himself to the Infirmary for 5 years. Later, this was relaxed to 3 years if he guaranteed not to practise in the area for a further 2 years. On the 24th April, 1851 the Minutes record that the House Surgeon:

> *"...be requested not, in future, to attend any out-patients under any consideration whatever as greatly increasing inconvenience results from the practice." "Further that he be particularly instructed not to supply medicine or advice to patients except on the recommendation of the Committee as such a practice has been found to lead to much irregularity and abuse of the institution."*[2]

On the 15th March, 1854 it occurred to the Committee that this policy was denying assistance to many deserving cases who were unable to come to the Infirmary. They decided that out-patients need not attend before the Committee if an Honorary Medical Officer certified that they were not fit to do so. After *"careful enquiry"* had been made of the patient's *"pecuniary circumstances"* the House Surgeon could visit them but *"never on any account but at the request of the Committee."*[2]

In 1855 the Minutes record that:

> *"It having been proved before the Committee that the House Surgeon had neglected his duty in not attending a patient who had been burnt and thereby seriously injured and that he had kept irregular hours and greatly neglected his duty; it is resolved that the Secretary give the House Surgeon notice to resign his situation in three months."*

Thus Mr. George Stratton Symmons was appointed to succeed Mr. Howell Evans at a salary of £100 per annum. Two weeks after commencing his duties Mr. Symmons was reprimanded by the Committee for being absent from the Infirmary *"from 6pm on Saturday until 2pm on Monday"* attending a patient for a private practitioner. On being reminded of the Rule and the conditions of his appointment Mr. Symons replied that they were *"unwarrantable and uncourteous"* to which the Committee replied that they were neither.

Mr Symmons was not terminated and was still in post when the new Infirmary opened in 1858.

The Rule was further relaxed when, on the 12th August, 1857, it was resolved that:

> *"In any case of cholera or other sudden emergency the House Surgeon be permitted to attend the patient at his or her residence when sent for and report the case or cases at the next weekly meeting."*[2]

The duties of the House Surgeon were multifarious. He was to:

> *"...fix tickets over each bed specifying the name and age of the patient, the date of admission, physician or surgeon by whom attended, and the diet prescribed."*[1]

He had to:

> *"...visit all the wards beginning not later than 9 o'clock, be ready to report the state of the patients to the physicians and surgeons, keep a diary of all such cases as they shall direct, make or cause to be made up the medicines and administered according to their respective prescriptions and particularly to attend to the ventilation of the house."*[1]

He was also to:

> *"...prepare and keep in each ward for the use of the physicians and surgeons the ward diet list and deliver an abstract thereof to the Matron daily; keep a book in which all orders for instruments, drugs, spirits of wine, brandy or wine for the use of the Dispensary amounting to 10 shillings or upwards be entered by him."*[1]

Such orders were not to be given until signed by a physician or surgeon.

He was ordered not to:

> *"...absent himself during the usual hours of attendance of the physicians and surgeons, nor during the absence of the Matron, nor without leaving a note in the Dispensary stating where he may be met with, nor for more than 4 hours at a time without an assurance from the physician or surgeon that they will attend when necessary during his absence, nor remain out of the House after 12 o'clock at night without the consent of the Committee."*[1]

He had to:

> *"...send a written notice to the physician or surgeon on the Saturday preceding their week of attendance and for all consultations for which the Rules require summonses taking care that they may be daily issued. On the admission of every casualty, or any other surgical emergency he, or in his absence his apprentice, shall send a written notice to the surgeon of the week and until the patient has been visited by the surgeon of the week he shall be considered under the care of the House Surgeon excepting as to the performance of a capital operation."*[1]

He was to:

> *"...carefully inspect all the medical and surgical instruments, utensils and articles when brought into the House and reject such as are not proper and use all means in his power to prevent damage, waste or embezzlement."*[1]

Nor was he to:

> *"...suffer gaming in any part of the house nor anything but the proper business to be done in the Dispensary."*[1]

He was allowed 2 apprentices for a three year period but he was bound to transfer them to his successor if he left during the term of their apprenticeship. These young men were presumably training to become apothecaries or, perhaps, preparing to take the membership examination of a College of Surgeons. In July, 1850 William Lewis and Thomas Hughes were admitted to the Infirmary as apprentices and in May, 1851 Abel Evans joined them on a trial basis. In September, 1855 we read in the Minutes that Abel Evans had asked the Committee if he could leave *"before the full term of 3 years to prosecute his studies in London on condition of his making up lost time in the vacation."*[2] Permission was refused. The parents or guardians of the apprentices were to provide them with *"board, washing and lodging."* The Infirmary would pay them £2 per year but they had to pay £50 into the funds of the Infirmary. The House Surgeon received £30 at the beginning of the apprenticeship and £20 at the end. He had to report any *"flagrant misbehaviour"* on the part of his apprentice to the Committee who might dismiss them if suitable *"remonstrances"* failed to effect an improvement in their conduct. One apprentice was to:

> *"...station himself in the Dispensary to attend to business there and to see that nothing is taken from it improperly."*[1]

The apprentices were enjoined to *"strictly observe and submit"* to the same rules as the House Surgeon.

While the House Surgeon's apprentices were a form of cheap labour, hence the Committee's refusal to allow the apprentice to go to London, the Honorary Staff was allowed to have 2 pupils *"whose names shall be entered in the Minutes to see the practice of the institution."* These may have been senior medical students who lived locally and wanted to gain experience in their vacation.

> *"Whilst in the house (their respective masters being absent) they shall obey the directions of the House Surgeon....they shall not conduct themselves disrespectfully or improperly towards any officer of the House, or Matron, or any servant, nurse or patient, nor obtrude themselves unnecessarily into any part of the House to which their duties do not lead such as the Dispensary, kitchen or household departments. They shall not at any time go into the women's wards unaccompanied by the House Surgeon or Matron, except in cases of*

> *absolute necessity....they shall perform no operations except the trivial ones of bleeding, extracting teeth etc. They shall dress the patients requiring it..... and shall willingly and faithfully render all assistance they can whenever required. The Consulting rooms of the House shall be the proper sitting rooms of the pupils when not otherwise occupied and they are strictly enjoined not to create confusion, disorder or disturbance therein. If any pupil shall so far forget himself as to appear in the House in a state of inebriation, he shall be instantly dismissed, on such being proved before the Committee without the possibility of reinstatement on any account whatever."*[1]

So much for nineteenth century opinion of medical students! However, it was possible to obtain reinstatement for less serious offences:

> *"...which shall never take place except he first send a written and respectful apology, through the Secretary, expressing contrition for his fault and requesting to be reinstated on a promise of amendment for the future."*[1]

Thus there is no doubt that the establishment, its staff, and the patients were subject to a rigorous system of supervision. The nurses would, undoubtedly, prior to the introduction of more formal training in the 1880s have received informal instruction from the medical staff who would, naturally, have been anxious that they should be competent to carry out the prescribed treatment and there is nothing in the record to suggest that the medical staff were unhappy with the nursing care their patients received.

In the early years detailed lists of cases and outcomes were presented by the House Surgeon at the Annual General Meeting. The publication of outcomes was dropped in the early 1880s and lists of cases treated were dropped in 1913 by which time the House Surgeon had been restyled the "Resident Medical Officer".

During the year ending in December, 1849 77 inpatients were treated of whom only 1 died from a fractured base of skull; 8 outpatients died of the 470 treated *"within the cognition"* of the House Surgeon. In 1870 140 inpatients were treated of whom 4 died; 2 being moribund at the time of admission; 2 were discharged as *"being of unsound mind"* and 134 were discharged *"cured or considerably relieved."* In 1881, the earliest record of operations, we read that *"9 difficult operations and 66 tooth extractions"* were performed and in only 1 case did the patient die – 1 of 2 cases of herniotomy. In 1882 12 operations were performed: ovariotomy 1, herniotomy 1, amputation through arm 2, removal of breast 2, cataract 2, epithelioma 1, and caries 3. It seems that these patients may all have survived because the causes of death of in-patients were given: tetanus 1, fractured spine 1, exhaustion 2. phthisis 2, hemiplegia 1. The following year the outcomes of surgery were not so gratifying: ovariotomy 1 – died 1, abdominal exploration 1 – died 1, hernia 3 – died 2, lithotomy 1 – died 1, amputations 5 – cured 5.[3] By this time anaesthetic technique was becoming more refined but, in 1858, the use of chloroform was still uncommon enough to rate a mention in the local newspapers. On the 28th May, 1858 the **Carmarthen Journal** reported that:

> *"The operation of lithotomy under chloroform was successfully performed at the Infirmary on an aged person and a stone weighing 1½ozs removed."*[4]

The Carmarthen House Surgeon was usually honest enough to report that his totals excluded patients whose *"letters"* `were renewed at the end of 2 months. Many hospitals included these patients and thus were able to present inflated totals and correspondingly decreased mortality rates. It is interesting to read that in May, 1899 the House Surgeon was authorized to purchase a Thomas's splint.

A very popular item of equipment found in most hospitals at this time and purchased by the Infirmary in April, 1871 was:

"Pulvermach's Patent Galvanic"
with chair bands, belts and pocket batteries

"Electricity is Life

These highly improved inventions render Electricity perfectly self-applicable in a mild continuous form and are extremely efficacious no shock or unpleasant sensation being experienced whereby it becomes a true fountain of health and vigour, speedily soothing agonizing pains, reanimating torpid limbs and reviving the sluggish functions of life."[3]

As far as medical treatment is concerned there is little specific information although lists of cases admitted did appear in the Annual Reports until 1913. We discovered, in the National Library of Wales, a Hospital Letter Book containing reports on the medical treatment of soldiers stationed in Carmarthen at the end of the 1840s. These were, in fact, letters to the War Office signed by John Hughes, F.R.C.S., Honorary Surgeon to the Infirmary for more than 40 years. As well as being of general interest they illustrate an important point, in the light of a controversy which raged amongst Infirmary subscribers throughout the 1870s, namely that the Honorary Medical Staff were very much general practitioners. We read in the Letter Book that a severe attack of influenza with a considerable degree of fever succeeded by bronchitis was treated with *"emetics, aperients and saline mixture followed by infus. gentian in acid sulph. dilut."* A case of catarrhus chronicus was treated with *"saline mixture for 3 days and cod liver oil for the next 4 days."*[5] In fact, such large quantities of cod liver oil were used in those days that it was usual to store it in tanks in the Dispensary. In the Minutes in 1871 we find T. C. Morris complaining that:

"Out-patient medicine runs away with large sums of money because of the enormous quantities of cod liver oil and quinine required."[2]

Agnes E. Pavey, when reading articles contributed to various medical journals and textbooks at this time, was struck by the dependence placed on whisky as a remedy for all "continued fevers and exhausted conditions":

"Whisky was prescribed in very large doses, often as much as a quart a day for one patient. It must have been rather

> *easy for nurses to obtain it and in their overworked and underpaid employment one can, perhaps, begin to understand why so many of them became noted tipplers."*[6]

Another very common treatment for all kinds of conditions was bleeding and leeching. Almost every week in the Minute Books amongst the lists of paid bills we find:

> *"Mary James – leechwoman – 7/-."*[2]

On the 14th July, 1851 the Minutes record that:

> *"...in as much as it is the opinion of the medical gentlemen who have examined John Roberts of Cwmcarnhowell, Llanelly he is not likely to receive benefit from the Infirmary but that the seaside will be more advantageous to his case."*

A *"subscription fund"* was set up for this purpose and there are numerous entries recording that *"one shilling and sixpence per week for one month be given free"* to assist patients in *"procuring board and lodging at the seaside."*

A Mr. Jennings was responsible, in 1872, for precipitating an argument which was not finally resolved until 1887. He aroused great indignation by stating that although he had been a subscriber for 15 years he had never been able to get a poor patient to accept:

> *"...a ticket for admission presumably because they thought they would be experimented upon or treated as if they were in a workhouse or gaol. Moreover, the principal justification for having an Infirmary in the town, namely to make available to the poor the services of not only the most eminent and accomplished surgeons in the town but also those of physicians of the highest class, men whose services would not be rendered under any other circumstances, no longer held true."*[4]

After Drs. Bowen (1858) and Lawrence (1862) had died there had been no physician at Carmarthen Infirmary. In view of the difficulty of finding pure physicians in Carmarthen he proposed that Rule 7 should read:

> *"...that the officers of the institution shall consist of, at least, 2 physicians and 2 surgeons, or 4 physicians or 4 surgeons."*[4]

The Rev. Latimer Jones had:

> *"...never heard of a person who objected to become an outdoor patient and to receive for nothing the advice and medicine he would have to pay heavily for in his own neighbourhood.*[4]

On out-patient days between 9 and 12 o'clock the Hall of the Infirmary was literally jammed with applicants and, at the weekly meetings, patients were always clamouring for admission – there was continual difficulty in finding room for in-patients. John Hughes F.R.C.S., the surgeon, was annoyed about the proposition to alter Rule 7:

> *"...the office should be more thought of than throwing it open to the whole town."*[4]

He agreed that a physician ought to be appointed and advertisements were placed in the medical press. One enquiry was received from a physician in Bournemouth but after he was told that there was no salary attached to the post *"nothing more was heard from him."* However, in 1873, Dr T. Lewis and Dr B.Timmins, both physicians, came to the town and joined the staff but both had retired by the time the matter finally came to head at the Annual General Meeting in 1887. It had been held up to this time that only an M.D. or an F.R.C.P. was entitled to act as a physician. John Hughes, F.R.C.S. and Dr. G. J. Hearder (the Medical Superintendent of St David's Hospital) pointed out that, since the Medical Registration Act of 1858, a *"legal medical practitioner"* was defined as *"a person registered under the Act"* and made this interesting and important statement:

> *"In large centres of population where they had much larger hospitals than in Carmarthen the rule defining physicians and surgeons was held of much importance. But in small towns like Carmarthen most of the medical men were general practitioners who took medical or surgical cases as they came. Therefore the difficulty of finding physicians in small towns was insuperable. For some time past there had been no physicians at the Infirmary and if the Rule had been rigidly carried out the medical patients would have received no attention at all as they were now attended to by the surgeons who should be strictly debarred from interfering with medical cases."*[4]

It was pointed out that the Rule respecting the physicians already included the words:

> *"...otherwise legally and properly qualified."*

and the Act of 1858 meant that, in fact, the whole controversy was irrelevant. Thus anybody registered under the Act who preferred to practise medicine rather than surgery would be eligible. This "general practitioner" system persisted well into the twentieth century, indeed, up to the appointed day on the 5th July, 1948 when many general practitioners became Consultants in the new National Health Service in their preferred specialty.

Over the 100 years of the Infirmary's existence many of the doctors served on the medical staff for the whole of their working lives. The founding surgeons were John Hughes (1818-1897), L.S.A.(1840), F.R.C.S.(1858), and James Rowlands (1814-1899), L.S.A.(1843), F.R.C.S. (1857). E. Hills Stacey (?c1790-1859) qualified L.S.A. in 1818 and M.R.C.S. (Eng.) in 1819 but did not achieve the Fellowship so little is known about him.

John Hughes was the son of a well-known Welsh preacher and was born in Cardiff. He trained at St Bartholomew's Hospital and was surgeon to the Infirmary, to the Police and one of the first Medical Officers of Health until his retirement in 1893. He became a Lieutenant Colonel of the Royal Carmarthen Artillery Militia, Chairman of the Board of Guardians and of the School Board, Commissioner of Income Tax and Justice of the Peace. Earlier in his career he was civil surgeon of a garrison in Ireland during the Potato Famine when there was an outbreak of scurvy. This was ably managed by Hughes who was thanked in General Orders by the Commander-in-Chief, The Duke of Wellington.[7]

James Rowlands was the son of the Vicar of Llanwch and went to school in Carmarthen. He trained at St. George's Hospital and then returned to Carmarthen were he practised for 40 years as surgeon to the Infirmary and the Prison and also as Coroner. He sat for 50 years on the Town Council and was an Alderman and Mayor in 1857. A political conservative he was much respected by all classes. He was the oldest member of the Town Council and of the medical profession in Carmarthenshire when illness compelled him to retire in 1899 and he died six months later at 51 King Street, Carmarthen. He married in 1835 and lived to celebrate his diamond wedding. He was survived by his wife and four married daughters and a son who had emigrated to the United States.[7]

The founding Physicians, Dr. Henry Lawrence, who died in 1862, and Dr. John Bowen did not achieve Membership or Fellowship of the Royal College of Physicians so little is known about them. Dr. Bowen died in 1858 before the new Infirmary opened and is known to have lived in King Street. Dr. Lawrence trained at St. Mary's Hospital and after serving as Assistant Surgeon to the 3rd Battalion, Grenadier Guards settled in Carmarthen living in Picton Terrace and became a J.P. Replacements were not found until Dr. T. Lewis, M.B. (1839), M.D., M.R.C.P. (1859) was appointed in 1873 and Dr B. Timmins, who trained at Barts qualified M.B.(1868) and proceeded M.D. in 1872 was appointed in 1875. Dr. Ll. M. Bowen-Jones was appointed in 1882 and retired in 1912.[8] Dr. Bowen-Jones trained at Guy's Hospital and qualified L.R.C.P., M.R.C.S. in 1878. He became Medical Officer of Health on the retirement of John Hughes in 1893.

The surgeons were joined by E. Parry Davies, who had trained in Dublin, in 1866, L.M. (Dublin 1865), M.R.C.S. (Eng. 1865) and served until 1888, and W. Lewis Hughes, L.S.A.(1874), M.R.C.S.

(1875) who had trained at The London Hospital and joined the staff in 1880.[8]

In 1891 the Annual Reports ceased to classify the medical staff as physicians or surgeons when Dr. Ll. M. Bowen-Jones, R.G. Price, M.D. (1891), M.R.C.P. (died 1913), W.L. Hughes and E.R. Williams are listed as the active 'Medical Officers' of the Infirmary.

The first formally trained specialist to be appointed was Mr. W.F. Brook, M.R.C.S. (1887). L.S.A. (1886), F.R.C.S. (1889) of Swansea in 1913. Mr. Brook trained at St Thomas's and became the most prominent surgeon of his day in South Wales. He operated at Swansea General Hospital, Carmarthen Infirmary, Glamorgan County Infirmary and Port Talbot General Hospital. Dr James. J. Healy, M.B., M.Ch. was the second; appointed Consulting Ophthalmic Surgeon in 1921. At that time he was the only Eye Surgeon west of Swansea. He trained in Edinburgh under Sir George Benny and joined the Armed Forces in 1915 serving in Mesopotamia and India. In 1917 he was appointed Consulting Ophthalmic Surgeon to Northern Command based at Catterick Camp and, after the War, was appointed to the Durham Eye Infirmary. The third specialist was Mr E. Alban Evans, M.R.C.S., L.R.C.P. (1899) who trained at Guy's Hospital and was appointed Consulting ENT Surgeon in 1924.[9]

A Gynaecologist trained at University College Hospital, Mr. J. Lloyd-Davies, M.B.(1912), M.C.O.G. 1934, F.R.C.S.Ed. (1926) was appointed in 1934. The tendency to specialize really began in the 1930s necessitated by advances in medical science. The first radiologist with a specialist diploma, D.M.R.E. (Liverpool, 1925), Dr. Iwan Davies, was appointed in 1938. Two Bacteriologists joined the staff in 1941; an Orthopaedic Surgeon in 1942; a Psychiatrist and a Pathologist in 1943. After 5 July 1948, 3 specialist Anaesthetists, 2 Chest Physicians, a Dermatologist and a Radiotherapist were appointed by the Welsh Regional Hospital Board now responsible for Consultant appointments under the new National Health Service.

Dr. Healy told us that Dr. Edward R. Williams (appointed in 1891 - retired in 1933) and Dr. Charles P. Parry (appointed in 1898 - retired in 1942 – died 1947) were the leaders of the profession in Carmarthen at that time and were very much in control of the Infirmary. Both were general practitioners and practised, with Dr. J.R.S. Webb, from Castle Hill House, 1, Spilman Street adjacent to the County Offices. Dr. Williams qualified, L.R.C.P.(Lond), M.R.C.S.(Eng.) in 1882 at St. Bartholomew's Hospital. Dr Parry qualified at Edinburgh University in 1889, M. B., Ch. M. and proceeded M.D. in 1891. Dr. Parry's son, C.F. Parry, qualified L.R.C.P., M.R.C.S. at Guy's Hospital in 1925 and joined the staff. He had an interest in radiology and obtained the D.M.R.D. specialist diploma in 1945 and set up the first training school for Radiographers at the Infirmary on the 1st July, 1948. It is important to realize that all these doctors were true "generalists" and could turn their hands to anything that came their way – medicine, surgery and obstetrics and gynaecology.[9]

Drs. C. A. Basker, R. T. Martin and Alan Trevor Jones had a general practice in Furnace House. Dr. Martin left in 1926 to become a Consultant Physician in Bournemouth and Dr. D.H. Lloyd joined the practice. Dr. Alan Trevor Jones later became Chief Medical Officer to the Welsh Regional Hospital Board and eventually Provost of the Welsh National School of Medicine in Cardiff. He trained in Cardiff and at University College Hospital qualifying in 1924. He obtained the M.R.C.P. and then proceeded M.D. in the University of London in 1927 and was elected F.R.C.P. He also obtained the D.P.H. Dr. J.R.E. James, joined the practice in 1933 having trained in Cardiff and at The London Hospital and became County Obstetrician in 1936. He developed into a specialist Obstetrician and Gynaecologist, acquiring an F.R.C.S.Ed (1942) and an M.R.C.O.G. in 1949 on the way, under the aegis of Professor Miles Phillips, later Chairman of the Management Committee, who had retired to Laugharne, in 1939, from the Chair of Midwifery in Sheffield. Professor Phillips worked indefatigably in the Maternity Department, which opened in 1937 and was named after him, throughout the Second World War. Mr. J. Lloyd-Davies was originally the Schools Medical Officer in Carmarthen and then became a Consultant Gynaecologist in Swansea maintaining his connection with the Infirmary. Dr. D.H. Lloyd, gave up general practice to work at the Infirmary and became a full-time Consultant General Surgeon on the appointed day. Dr. T. E. Jones-Davies became a Consultant Physician. All these men had been members of the Honorary Medical Staff of the Infirmary.[9]

These two practices in Castle Hill House and Furnace House provided the Honorary Medical Staff to the Infirmary. It was very much a closed shop. Anyone fortunate enough to be able to purchase a partnership in either of these practices was guaranteed to be taken on to the staff of the Infirmary.

Dr. Healy, who acted as Chairman of the Management Committee from 1946 to 1948, told us that in the 1920s and 1930s there were very few medical cases in the Infirmary; the call was largely for surgery which was managed by Mr. Brooks who was later joined by Mr. Howell Gabe. The main work of the Infirmary was in General Surgery, Urology (Mr. Brook and Mr. Gabe); ENT (Mr. C. P. Robinson), Ophthalmology (Dr. Healy & Dr G.S. Forrester) and Obstetrics and Gynaecology (Mr. J. Lloyd Davies). The requirement that a patient be recommended by a Governor was a mere formality in Carmarthen but there were potential difficulties which are discussed in the chapter dealing with finance and administration. Any medical man who wanted to admit a case was able to do so.[9]

All the Honorary Medical Staff were ex-officio members of the House Committee and the relationship between the medical members and lay members was usually harmonious except for some disagreement over eligibility, between the doctors and the Committee between 1930 and 1933, and between the doctors themselves in 1944 when Dr Healy, as one of the most senior physicians, was appointed Chairman to try and find an agreement. The doctors were usually supported by the Management Committee when they wanted to buy new equipment or, otherwise, to improve the service. Carmarthen was a small place and everybody mixed socially. General Practitioners' cases were approved by one of the Consultants. Happily, paperwork was very limited – there were two part-time Honorary Secretaries and they did most of it. There were 2 or 3 private beds but large numbers of patients who would have been admitted today "didn't get in and didn't want to." People were afraid to have operations so the demand was low. It was only just before the Second World War that people began to think that hospitals could be of any positive benefit to them.[9]

General Practitioners gave "rag and bottle" (ether dripped onto a cloth pad covering the patient's mouth and nose) anaesthesia: *'some, like Dr. Adam Lewis of King Street, were good but most were hopeless.'* The patients tended to vomit for hours afterwards and surgeons, particularly Ophthalmologists, preferred to use local anaesthesia. Cocaine was first used in 1884, procaine in 1905 and lignocaine in the 1940s. Before the Second World War nurses were only very rarely trained for specialties. Most nurses in Carmarthen were farmers' or industrial workers' daughters. Theatre technique was, if anything, more meticulous than at present. Strict aseptic techniques had been introduced in the 1890s and, by the early twentieth century, surgeons were wearing gowns and gloves. There were no antibiotics if anything went wrong. Another major problem was that most patients had very little notion of personal hygiene and could not understand the importance of not interfering with dressings. They were always reluctant to remove layers of woollen vests and clothing they hadn't parted from for months. One inpatient, a man from Pembrokeshire, was believed to change his shirt only once per year. After cataract operations patients tended to wrap shawls around their heads. They were required to remain in bed for 2 or 3 weeks but many, particularly the men, were often found outside the Infirmary smoking cigarettes. The only tuberculous patients admitted were those suitable for surgery – rib resections, excision of tuberculous lymph glands and aspiration of joints! There was no real thoracic surgery until the Second World War and then it was performed by the general surgeons.[9]

When Mr. Neville Chamberlain, Prime Minister, declared at 11am on the 3rd September, 1939 that:

> *"...this country is now at war with Germany."*

the Infirmary joined the national Emergency Medical Service Scheme which had been organized by the Ministry of Health for dealing with war casualties. The hospital was graded "1A" which necessitated a considerable increase in the number of beds available paid for by the

Ministry. It was pointed out that this would mean overcrowding but it was to be regarded solely as a wartime emergency measure. At the outbreak of war the Ministry of Health instructed that all patients who were fit enough should be discharged so, within a few hours, 80% of patients were taken to their homes. The Ministry had also asked that the hospital provide an underground Operating Theatre and a 'gas cleansing station' and this was arranged on the lower floor. By the end of October 1939, as no serious emergencies had arisen and as it had been shown that the Infirmary could be rapidly evacuated in time of need, the Government allowed normal working to resume.[3]

In 1941 the Annual Report notes that:

> *"...a very interesting development has been the admission of a number of medical students to pursue their studies at the Infirmary. Owing to the difficulties experienced in many larger hospitals in many well-known centres it became necessary to use smaller hospitals for training work. It is gratifying to learn that the facilities and help we were able to give in this particular matter have been very considerable and have been valued as being of a very high quality."*[3]

Hospital legend has it that if an interesting case came in at night the porter would go over to the house in The Parade where the students were sleeping and pull a string attached to their ankles and left dangling out of their windows.

The Resident Medical Officer was called up and the Mayoress of Carmarthen (Dr Anne Davies) stood in until a well-known refugee Czechoslovakian doctor, Dr. H. Feldstein, was appointed in 1941. Professor Miles Phillips, giving his Presidential Address in 1942 commented: "*...I venture to say that his recruitment was one of the few bright spots in the ghastly mess that Hitler has perpetrated.*" As would be expected, the younger men joined H.M. Forces and the older men stayed behind and continued to run the Infirmary. At the victorious conclusion of the war in Europe in May, 1945 the Infirmary had treated 1,728 Emergency Medical Service inpatients and over 4,000 outpatients mostly sick or wounded servicemen and also casualties of the bombing, by the German Luftwaffe, of towns and cities in South Wales during the early years of the war. After D-Day there were usually 40 to 50 soldiers in House with occasional Royal Air Force and Royal Navy personnel. The General Office held the soldiers' paybooks, issued pocket money and submitted weekly returns to the War Office. "Late" passes were issued to enable the walking wounded to go into the town to the cinema. They were required to wear "Hospital Blues"; blue suit, white shirt and red tie. This "uniform" for convalescent soldiers was compulsory in all military hospitals throughout both World Wars. One or two very severely incapacitated soldiers were taken out by volunteer staff in wheelchairs borrowed from the Red Cross. After VE day the Ministry now asked that the Infirmary only admit local cases of illness and accident amongst soldiers on leave.[3]

More than 80% of Voluntary Hospital Medical Staff were appointed Consultants in the National Health Service in July, 1948. The remaining 20% became Senior Hospital Medical Officers. There was an appeal process but everybody in Carmarthen was happy.[9]

We put it to Dr. Healy that it had been said of the voluntary hospitals that many of the specialists listed in the Annual Reports never saw patients at all and that most of the work was done by the Resident Medical Officer and local general practitioners who would be reluctant to call in a consultant because no fee would be offered. This resulted in general practitioners attempting surgery beyond their competence. Dr Healy replied that, in Carmarthen, this was, usually, not the case. He reminded us that between 1915 and 1933 the Infirmary did not employ a Resident Medical Officer. He recalled only one serious complaint about a child being neglected because the doctor on duty could not be found and it was decided, as the hospital was becoming busier to advertise for a Resident Medical Officer. All the specialists did their regular sessions and were, usually, available on call. He did agree that many were self-taught and continued with general practice. Certainly, some of the new Consultants appointed in 1948 did not have enough specialist experience and would not have been appointed if they had not been on the staff of the Infirmary at the time.[9]

Dr Healy took the view that the National Health Service gave much greater scope for talented men like D. C. Williams, M.Ch., F.R.C.S. who was working at a small hospital in Cardigan and, also, for demobilized servicemen returning to the area. He felt that modern medicine had become too complex and too expensive, and the demand on services too great, for groups of local volunteers to continue to manage as they had done in the past. Government funding, full-time experienced administrators and full-time consultant specialists were now essential to enable the service to expand into modern accommodation and benefit all patients with the continuing advances in medical knowledge and technology.[9]

When we spoke with Dr. Healy the National Health Service had been in existence for almost 20 years and during that time these advances had been staggering both in scope and magnitude. Prior to 1948 there were only a few drugs available – salicylates (aspirin) for rheumatic fever, digoxin for heart disease, and the antibiotics; penicillin, the sulphonamides and, later, streptomycin.[10] Remarkably for that era, insulin for diabetes had been isolated by Frederick Banting and Charles Best, working in Toronto in 1922, for which they won the Nobel Prize for Medicine in 1923.

During the first decade, and thereafter, new antibiotics were introduced in rapid succession and the major problem of bacterial resistance had not yet arisen. Cortisone and ACTH, Vitamin B_{12}, chlorpromazine, polio immunisation, contraceptive pills, thiazide diuretics and effective treatment of blood pressure were all introduced[10] and adopted in practice at the West Wales General Hospital.

Technical developments in the 1950s included hip replacements which were first performed at the West Wales General Hospital in 1971 by Mr. R.L. Rees. The first kidney transplant was performed in 1954 by Dr. Joseph Murray at the Peter Bent Brigham Hospital in Boston, Massachusetts for which he was awarded the Nobel Prize for Medicine in 1990. Surgery for rheumatic heart disease, heart-lung machines, ultrasound developed from wartime sonar and used initially in obstetrics and the image intensifier were also introduced. The availability of radioisotopes led to the development of nuclear medicine and, at this time, radiotherapy, which dates back to the early 20th century, gradually became more refined and sophisticated. The first medical linear accelerator was installed at the Hammersmith Hospital in 1952. Both modalities are now available at Singleton Hospital, Swansea.

The elucidation of the structure of DNA at the Cavendish Laboratory, Cambridge by Francis Crick and James Watson in 1953 led to a veritable explosion in the study of genetics and the ongoing possibility of clinical application. Crick and Watson shared the Nobel Prize for Medicine with Maurice Wilkins, the X-ray crystallographer, in 1962. Now joint clinics by the Paediatricians and Physicians are held at Glangwili with visiting Consultant Geneticists. Treatments based on genetic manipulation are slow to materialise but may well, eventually, revolutionise the management of many conditions including cancer.

In 1954 Lawrence Curtiss, a physics undergraduate at the University of Michigan, invented a process by which flexible glass fibres could be coherently bundled to convey a whole image. This led to Basil Horowitz at the same University developing a flexible gastroscope in 1957. Flexible instruments rapidly replaced the rigid endoscopes which had a 100 year history and, more recently, had been using the lens system developed by Professor Harold Hopkins at the University of Reading. Fibreoptic endoscopes are now enormously sophisticated and capable of a whole range of diagnostic and therapeutic manoeuvres throughout the gastrointestinal, genital, urinary and respiratory tracts and also the skeletal system. Recent capital developments at the West Wales General Hospital include the provision of a new Theatre complex comprising a new Endoscopy Suite, a 23 bed Day Case Surgical Unit and a new General Theatre and the planned refurbishment of the old Theatre Suite at a cost of £5.3 million. The old Endoscopy Suite and Day Theatre facility opened in 1995 will be remodelled and used to provide a comprehensive Urology service much of which will be endoscopic.

Contrast media became available in the early 1950s and are injected for diagnostic purposes by the Seldinger Technique, described by the

Swedish radiologist in 1953, of percutaneous puncture and passage of catheters into blood vessels for diagnostic purposes and called angiography. Later, this technique developed therapeutic possibilities such as balloon angioplasty, insertion of stents and embolisation. It continues to play a part in the rapidly developing specialties of invasive cardiology and interventional radiology which are available at Morriston Hospital, Swansea. It makes sense for some specialties to be made available only in Regional Centres with catchment populations of, at least, one million generating sufficient patients to maintain skills and justify expenditure. Furthermore, it has been clearly shown that very ill patients do significantly better in high volume institutions with all subspecialties available.

In the second decade, tranquillisers and Librium, growth hormone, measles and oral polio vaccine became available. The first liver transplant was performed by Thomas Starzl in Denver, Colorado. in 1963. In 1967, Christian Barnard at Groote Schuur Hospital, South Africa carried out the first heart transplant. Coronary artery bypass grafting and haemodialysis for renal failure were introduced into routine practice. Cardiac surgery services are provided at Morriston Hospital, Swansea and in Cardiff and haemodialysis at the West Wales General Hospital.

Computerised axial tomography (CT scanning) was developed by Godfrey Hounsfield in England working at the E.M.I. Laboratories, in 1972, for which he was awarded the Nobel Prize for Medicine in 1979. Insufficient funding led to the Germans (Siemens) and Americans (G.E.) producing the machines commercially. A CT scanner was installed in Carmarthen in 1987 and replaced with Spiral CT in 1997 which produces three-dimensional images at high speed.

In 1976 the Histamine-2 Receptor Antagonists, such as Cimetidine, were introduced for the treatment of peptic ulcers dramatically reducing the need for surgery. The Proton Pump Inhibitors, for example - Omeprazole, were even more effective and came on the market in the late 1980s.

In 1980 Sir Peter Mansfield at the University of Nottingham and Paul

Lauterbur at the University of Illinois had developed magnetic resonance imaging (MRI) for which they shared the Nobel Prize for Medicine in 2003. Again, commercial development took place in Germany and the United States. Magnetic Resonance Imaging is available in conjunction with the Compass Group at Prince Philip Hospital. At about the same time Positron Emission Tomography or PET scanning, which dates back to the 1950s, began to be used clinically and is now available at Singleton Hospital, Swansea. It is an invasive technique requiring the injection of radioactive glucose which is produced at considerable expense in a cyclotron and is, therefore, not widely available. Small primary and secondary cancerous tumours, not detectable on CT & MRI scans, rapidly metabolise the glucose and show up as hotspots on the scan. The technique is also used to evaluate heart and brain function. Also in the fourth decade, the first "test-tube baby" was born and in 1982 the first case of AIDS was reported.

In 1987, Philippe Mouret in France, performed the first human laparoscopic cholecystectomy made possible by the development, in 1982, of the solid-state video-camera. The notion of laparoscopy had been around for 200 years and diagnostic laparoscopy had been performed, mostly by Gynaecologists, since the early 20th century. This signalled the beginning of minimally invasive or "keyhole" surgery which has revolutionised the practice of surgery. It is now possible, with the development of sophisticated instrumentation, to perform a huge variety of major procedures that formerly required a week or two in hospital as Day Cases or with a much reduced length of stay. The rapidly developing science of robotics has now begun to play a major role and allows a surgeon to operate without the assistants who currently hold and manipulate the camera and other instruments. Broadband technology is permitting "telecollaborative" surgery. For example a surgeon in London, or even overseas, may now assist or even operate on a patient in Carmarthen without being physically present. Laparoscopic surgery became widespread in England and Wales during the 1990s and there are now hospital departments that offer surgery, using these methods, to the "unborn patient". The West Wales General Hospital provides a wide range of laparoscopic operations and more than 70% of elective procedures are carried out on a Day Case basis.

In 1988 the MMR (Measles, Mumps, Rubella) vaccine became available and the Hepatitis C virus was discovered. In 1997 the first mammalian clone, Dolly the sheep, was born starting a profound ethical debate.[10]

In the 1950s, 60s and 70s, and before, consultant ward rounds took place once or twice per week and were extremely formal. Patients lay quietly in freshly made beds. Televisions and radios were switched off. Maintenance men were told to stop whatever they were doing and a student nurse was sent out to tell the groundsman not to mow the grass or make any agricultural noises whatsoever. Hospital practice was arranged on the old "firm" system so the consultant, wearing a suit, was accompanied by an entourage of his junior staff all wearing white coats. Mr. A. Henry (Harry) Millard (1915-1975) was the archetypal consultant surgeon at this time. He arrived in his Rolls Royce, which he parked at the Fire Exit to Ward Block 1. No one else was allowed to park in this area, now a consultants' car park, in case they should collide with the Rolls. He was tall, slightly built, almost completely bald and was always immaculately dressed in a pinstripe suit with a fresh flower in his buttonhole. He had been a Senior Registrar at the Hospital for Sick Children, Great Ormond Street as well as at the United Cardiff Hospitals so undertook major neonatal and paediatric surgery as well as the whole spectrum of general surgery. He had served in the Royal Army Medical Corp as a surgeon, in the rank of Major, and was attached to the 8th Army throughout the North African and Italian campaigns. He could be an abrasive character, particularly in the Operating Theatre, but had a heart of gold. His ward rounds were very entertaining and he was an excellent teacher. His standard retort to his juniors when they suggested management plans that he considered foolish was: *"My dear boy, you might as well fan his umbilicus with a bowler hat."* At the conclusion of his ward round a student nurse would serve coffee and toast which would be taken in sister's office - anathema to modern academic nurses!

The only Operating List which survives from this period is dated 5th April, 1972. Surgeon: Mr. A. Henry Millard; Anaesthetist: Dr. H.B. Maliphant. Start time was 9am and there were 13 cases. Right varicose veins, biopsy left breast lump, excision angioma on back, left retrograde pyelogram, 2 cystoscopies, a Hellers operation, 3 cholecystectomies, a prostatectomy, excision of pilonidal sinus and resuture of wound. The cholecystectomies and the prostatectomy were, of course, open procedures. The lists often continued into the evening but nobody minded or even commented. Dr. Henry Maliphant liked to boast that his medical school, St George's, had the best address of all the London medical schools – No 1, Hyde Park Corner. He was not pleased when St. George's moved to Tooting! He enjoyed criticising the facility and always prefaced his remarks by stating:

> *"This is the only hospital in the country with 3 counties dependent on it, but...* (e.g.) *there's never a bloody artery forceps in the anaesthetic room."*

Mr. David Clowes (D.C.) Williams (?1906-1992) qualified in 1929 in Cardiff, obtained the FRCS in 1944 and the M.Ch. in 1953. He was quiet, unassuming, of distinguished appearance and a very talented surgeon who worked mainly in Priory Street until it closed to acute cases in early 1969. The senior physician was Glan Davies, M.D., F.R.C.P. who qualified in Cardiff in 1939 and still lives in Nantgaredig. He was a distinguished and erudite man who was a fine after-dinner speaker. Richard (Dickie) L. Rees, F.R.C.S. (died 2004) was in charge of Orthopaedics. He trained at the Middlesex Hospital qualifying in 1941 and, after retirement, spent a period as Professor of Orthopaedics in Riyadh, Saudi Arabia. These were the days, before internal and external fixation of fractures, when young men who had fractured their femurs, often in motorbike accidents, spent many weeks in hospital beds on traction. The highlight of their day was when wives and girlfriends visited, the curtains would be drawn around the beds and the traction apparatus would begin to rattle and shake! These goings-on were tactfully ignored by the ward staff. Other significant figures in the hospital at this time were Dr. James Clough Davies, Consultant in Geriatric Medicine; Salathiel Morgan, F.R.C.S.(Ed), Consultant ENT Surgeon and Kenneth Keay, Consultant Paediatrician.

Patients knew little about their conditions and no effort was made to enlighten them. The cultivation of the mystique of medical practice can be attributed to knowledge of the power of the placebo effect, which remains significant to this day, and the lack of effective treatments. There was no monitoring of outcomes or of individual performance. It was just naturally assumed by everyone from Consultant downwards that patients, whose expectations were low, received the best care available. In fact, the authors and others who worked at Glangwili during this period can only recall that operative morbidity and mortality rates were extremely low.

No patient would have thought of cross-examining a consultant on his results as patients are expected to do today. Most treatments were based on anecdotal reports. Randomised controlled trials (RCTs) the key to evidence-based medicine, now so crucial to medical practice, were in their infancy. Indeed, the British Medical Research Council's trial of streptomycin for pulmonary tuberculosis, published in 1948, has been proposed as the first in which random numbers were used and the allocation of patients was effectively concealed. However, it now seems that sporadic RCTs had appeared before 1948. The first of these was a trial of the serum treatment of diphtheria by the Danish Nobel Laureate Johannes Fibiger (1867-1928) in 1898. Fibiger emphasised random allocation as a pivotal methodological principle. Archibald Cochrane (1909-1988), vigorously promoted RCTs and his seminal work, based on his 1966 Nuffield Trust Rock Carling Lecture "Effectiveness and Efficiency", published in 1972 earned him an international reputation.[11] He worked initially at Llandough Hospital, Cardiff in the Medical Research Council's Pneumoconiosis Research Unit. In 1960 he was appointed Professor of Tuberculosis and Chest Diseases at the Welsh National School of Medicine renamed the University of Wales College of Medicine in 1984.

Numerous government-sponsored reports, on Hospital Medical Staffing (Platt, 1961), Royal Commission on Medical Education (Todd, 1968), Medical Administration (Hunter, 1972), Regulation of the Medical Profession (Merrison, 1975), NHS Management (Griffiths, 1983) and Medical Manpower (1987), had little effect on the way in which hospital consultants were trained and, subsequently, practised in the NHS. It remained an informal apprenticeship system with the "old boy" network playing its part and everyone "doing his best". This included young doctors working 120 hours and more per week. The Todd Report resulted in the pairing of the 12 London medical schools and their association with multi-faculty colleges of the University of London. New schools were founded in Nottingham, Leicester and Southampton. Since that time medical schools have sprung up all over the country: Brighton & Sussex, East Anglia, Hull/York, Keele, Peninsula (Plymouth/Exeter), Swansea and Warwick. Thus every other hospital is now a University Hospital and every other doctor is a Professor!

In 2003, the European Working Time Directive (EWTD) restricted the hours that doctors are permitted to work and has adversely affected those key elements in training – continuity of care and access to an adequate volume of cases. The length of specialist training seems likely to be shortened even further by the ongoing "Modernising Medical Careers" (MMC) initiative. All this will have the effect of reducing staffing levels and increasing costs.

Before and after 1948 continuing medical education (CME) had been supported by the medical Royal Colleges, undertaken on a voluntary basis and encouraged by the NHS which authorised paid study leave. In the United States CME dates from the late 1920s and the first mandatory programme was initiated in Urology in 1934 and was widespread by the end of the 1960s. The American Medical Association published its guide to good medical practice in 1957. In 2003, a statutory body, the Postgraduate Medical Education and Training Board was set up in London over the objections of the medical Royal Colleges whose activities it merely duplicates.

In the United Kingdom pressures resulting from European Union legislation led, in 1993, to the Calman Report – Sir Kenneth Calman was Chief Medical Officer at the Department of Health. The minimum length of specialist training was reduced to 7 years. More explicit training curricula were introduced and Registrar and Senior Registrar grades were merged into a single specialist registrar grade.[10] Crucially, a certificate of completion of specialist training was introduced as a requirement for inclusion on the Specialist Register set up by the General Medical Council on the 12th January, 1996. This became a legal requirement for appointment as a substantive, honorary or fixed-term consultant in the NHS.

In the late 1990s the public, its representatives in Parliament and the General Medical Council (GMC) were alarmed by a number of high profile malpractice cases, the Bristol Paediatric Cardiac Surgery scandal and the Shipman enquiry into the murder of possibly 250 patients by a general practitioner who committed suicide in prison in 2004. Despite the fact that Shipman was clearly an aberration the tabloid press waged a campaign of "doctor-bashing" with great relish. Sadly, this was met with silence by the leaders of the profession who conspicuously failed to speak out on behalf of the vast majority of hardworking, highly competent clinicians. The GMC responded by proposing that the registration and regulation of doctors should be made more robust and not simply based on a historical record of qualification. It was felt that each doctor should be able to regularly demonstrate that he is current in his knowledge, healthy, honest and practises in a quality assured environment according to the concepts of "Good Medical Practice" published by the GMC in 1995. This was accepted by government, which was preparing to impose its own solution, and may lead to the process of "revalidation" every 5 years based, in most cases, on the dubious process of the local annual appraisal of colleague by colleague. Annual appraisal became a requirement on the 1st April, 2003 and revalidation was to commence on the 1st April, 2005 and would have resulted in a doctor's "license" to practise being renewed or not.

The 1983 Medical Act was modified by Parliament in 2002 to permit the GMC to operate the new system of revalidation and licenses. By contrast, the majority of American Specialty Boards require "recertification" every 10 years, usually by examination. The American Board of Family Practice began the process in 1969 and recertification has been a requirement by most Boards since that time. It is interesting to note that, in 1982, the Royal College of General Practitioners was the first in the U.K. to introduce mandatory vocational training. At the time of writing Dame Janet Smith, a High Court judge, has criticised the GMC in her Shipman Report and the Department of Health has placed the revalidation arrangements on hold until a committee, chaired by Sir

Liam Donaldson, Chief Medical Officer, considers and perhaps modifies them in the light of the report's criticisms.

The West Wales General Hospital has, of course, been profoundly affected by all these developments. All Consultants now in post are included on the Specialist Register and subject to annual appraisal and probably quinquennial revalidation. A rigorous system of clinical governance is in place. Happily, clinicians are still trained at the bedside but with the reduction in working hours and the length of training coupled with the increasing degree of sub-specialisation and steeper learning curves it is likely that hospital practice and the way in which acute and emergency services are delivered will have to change to take account of consultants emerging from training whose experience is limited in depth and, more importantly, in breadth.

References:

[1] Rules & Regulations County Infirmary, Carmarthen, 1846, 1857 and subsequent revisions, Carmarthenshire Archives Service.

[2] Minute Books, County Infirmary, Carmarthen, 1846 to 1942, Carmarthenshire Archives Service.

[3] Annual Reports, County Infirmary, Carmarthen, 1846 to 1948, Carmarthenshire Archives Service.

[4] Carmarthen Journal, 1810 to date, (Microfilm) Carmarthen Reference Library.

[5] Hospital Letter Book, NLW MS 17388B, National Library of Wales.

[6] The Story of the Growth of Nursing as an Art, a Vocation and a Profession, Agnes Pavey, 1938, Faber & Faber.

[7] Lives of the Fellows, 1800 to 2002, Library of the Royal College of Surgeons of England.

[8] The Medical Directory, 1843 to 2004, Library of the Royal College of Surgeons of England.

[9] James J. Healy, M.B. M.Ch., Consulting Ophthalmologist to the County Infirmary, Carmarthen 1921 to 1948 and to the West Wales General Hospital, 1948 to 1957. Chairman of the Management Committee, Carmarthenshire Infirmary, 1st January, 1946 to 5th July 1948. Personal communication, 28th April, 1967.

[10] From Cradle to Grave, Fifty Years of the NHS, Geoffrey Rivett, 1997. King's Fund Publishing.

[11] Effectiveness & Efficiency, Archibald Cochrane, 1972. Nuffield Provincial Hospitals Trust.

CHAPTER VI

GOVERNING, FINANCING AND DEVELOPING THE COUNTY INFIRMARY, CARMARTHEN

The Infirmary was run by a House Committee consisting of 21 Governors who were elected at each Annual General Meeting for the ensuing year. Governors of the Infirmary were:

1. *annual subscribers of one guinea and upwards.*
2. *nominated representatives of congregations who make an annual collection of three guineas and upwards.*
3. *donors of ten guineas and upwards.*
4. *if the contribution amounts to twenty guineas and upwards the donor is a Governor for life.*[1]

The traditional way of enticing subscriptions was to allow subscribers to recommend patients for admission. The number of patients, out or in, the subscriber was permitted to have on the books at any one time was related to the amount of his donation or subscription. For example, the rules laid down that every subscriber of *"two guineas annually shall be entitled to recommend one indoor patient in the year and have three outdoor patients constantly on the books."* The subscribers were not always punctual in paying their subscriptions. At a Special General Meeting in January, 1848 the names of defaulters were read out. A **Carmarthen Journal** reporter who was present manifested considerable surprise at *"the respectability of the parties who were in arrears"* and expressed an earnest wish that they would *"see the propriety of paying in their respective amounts without delay."*[2] Every subscriber was supplied with a number of blank forms of recommendation *"commensurate with his subscription"* which he was to fill up and *"deliver to the patient he recommends."* The Honorary Physicians and Surgeons were allowed the privilege of subscribers of two guineas and were ex-officio members of the House Committee.[1]

Anyone was eligible to be elected President who had made a single donation of fifty guineas or an annual subscription of ten guineas. In the early years, only the most significant personages in a social sense were asked to fill the office which, in Carmarthen, meant either The Lord Dynevor or The Earl Cawdor. In later years more democratic, or rather meritocratic, principles operated and, perhaps with an eye to collateral benefits which might accrue to the Infirmary, distinguished persons were approached to fill the office on an annual basis. Sir Alfred Mond, M.P. for Carmarthen 1924 to 1928 who later became The Lord Melchett, one of the first Ministers of Health, presided at the Annual General Meeting in 1925 and, subsequently, presented the Infirmary with its first wireless installation. His Honour Judge J. Lloyd Morgan, K.C. presided in 1928 having started, with a handsome donation, a fund for providing an electric lift for patients installed in 1929. Lord & Lady Kylsant, whose home at Combe, Llanybri is now a Cheshire Home, were enthusiastic supporters of the Infirmary.

Similar criteria were used when selecting Trustees in whose name the permanent capital of the institution was held. There was no limit to the number of Vice Presidents – anybody making a single donation of 25 guineas or an annual subscription of 5 guineas. In later years, a donation of £1,000 would endow a bed above which a plaque would be fixed naming the bed after the donor. The names of people making generous gestures were printed boldly in the Annual Reports. In 1853 a large mahogany board, now in the Carmarthen Museum, was purchased on which the names of people making substantial donations or legacies were inscribed in gold lettering.

An Infirmary Banner, present whereabouts unknown, was presented by Henry Studt in 1880, which had a woven inscription stating:

> *"Blessed is he that considereth the poor, sick and needy."*[3]

Three members of the House Committee formed a quorum. In 1847 they met every Wednesday morning at 11 o'clock. Subsequently, the day and time was often changed. They had powers to

> *"...require the attendance of all persons connected therewith for examining and discharging tradesmen's and*

> *other accounts; to regulate the admission and discharge of patients and prepare all such matters and general statements as are proper to be laid before the general Meetings of Governors....and to conduct the affairs of the institution generally subject to the approval of the General Meetings."*[1]

Firstly, the Committee received and studied the House Surgeon's report which contained a detailed record of all admissions and discharges during the previous week along with details of outpatients seen and treated. Secondly, the "Visitors" report was discussed. Thirdly, "Visitors" were nominated for the following week and, fourthly, Governors' nominations of new patients were vetted and approved or denied. Finally, the payment of bills for the week was authorised and recorded in the Minutes. Staff salaries were paid quarterly. The policy of the Committee was to invite tenders for all supplies required on a regular basis, particularly of provisions, and then to award a contract. They were quick to complain if any item was found to be sub-standard.

A typical week's bill payments recorded in the Minutes is dated the 12th July, 1849:

Mrs. Rowlands for Diet	*£2 18s 9d*
Mary James for Leeches	*4s 0d*
John White for Gutta Percha	*£1 0s 3½d*
Mr. Melton for candles	*3s 0d*
C. Jones, Barber	*6s 5d*
J. White for Combs	*2s 7d*
D. Williams for Coffin	*£1 0s 0d*
Isaac Davies for Bed Chair	*£1 3s 0d*
Messrs. David & Co., Ironmongers	*£1 4s 0d*

In Carmarthen the Committee was generally prepared to accept any recommendations of the medical men who were the only people in town that had any knowledge of the workings of a voluntary hospital because they trained in one. It should not be assumed that this harmonious situation obtained in all voluntary hospitals where disagreements between the medical members and the lay members were often a major problem.

For religious, humanitarian and, other, perhaps less commendable reasons, or merely because the work was interesting, there were many subscribers willing to serve on the Committee. They were, of course, often elderly and retired – the work was an outlet for energies and abilities, hopefully, unaffected by the passing of years. Initially, no doubt, Governors were nominated for membership of the House Committee because they possessed qualifications, skills or influence which it was thought could be utilized for the benefit of the Infirmary. The first Honorary Treasurers, Thomas Charles Morris and his brother, William, were bankers. Their bank was later taken over by the National Provincial which, in turn, merged with the Westminster Bank to form the NatWest. Successive bank managers were always appointed Honorary Treasurers. They often, generously, refrained from making charges on frequently overdrawn accounts.

In the early years the Secretary was usually one of the less well-endowed subscribers. Although paid a small salary the post could hardly be described as full time and paper work was kept to a minimum. He worked directly under the instructions of the House Committee of which he was a member, dealing with correspondence, collecting subscriptions for which he was paid a 5% commission and keeping the Minutes and Accounts. Later he was required to provide "*security in the sum of £200 to the satisfaction of the Committee.*" The Secretaries served for surprisingly lengthy periods. Mr. John White, who had his own Pharmacy, was the first and served until his death 20 years later. His successor, Mr. Howell Howells, served for 27 years and was followed, after a short interval, by his son. In 1921 a "disagreement" arose between the Committee and the Secretary of the time regarding the accounts and it was decided that the post should become an Honorary one. Mr. John Richards, who had joined the House Committee in 1917 had volunteered. He was joined in 1924 by the retired Manager of the Bank, Mr. J. Arthur Jones, who had previously been Treasurer.

Records show that, almost invariably, members of the House Committee were re-elected at Annual General Meetings. It was with the Committee that real power resided. Certainly, it was not in their interest to limit the number of Governors as there was obviously no need to limit the funds. Indeed, if enough of the Governors thought it was necessary they could change the whole policy of the institution. Unless an attendance record was particularly bad, usually only death or removal from the area caused a vacancy. The main body of subscribers would soon have recognized that those who had become most familiar with the problems of running the Infirmary would be the most suitable for re-election. Thus, inevitably, they became a self-perpetuating body. Until the 1880s the House Committee elected a Chairman annually. Then it was decided that the interests of the institution would be better served by the appointment of a permanent chairman – subject to re-election at the Annual General Meeting. The first permanent Chairman was Mr. C.W. Jones although the date of his appointment is unclear. He was succeeded in 1891 by The Rev. Canon Charles Gilbert Brown, M.A., D.Sc., Principal of Trinity College, Carmarthen who dominated the scene until his death in 1924. He served for 37 years on the Committee and 33 years as Chairman. For the next 10 years Mr. Walter Lloyd, J.P. acted as Chairman until 1935 when he was replaced by The Rev. Waldo B. Lewis, B.A., Pastor of Penuel Church. A dispute between the Honorary Medical Staff and the Committee resulted in the appointment as Chairman in 1944 of Dr. James J. Healy who promised to try and work out an agreement. Dr. Healy would not discuss details but said the problem was one of personalities rather than principles and was related to responsibilities at the Infirmary.[3,4,5]

The House Committee concerned themselves with everything from rhubarb to politics. A certain Mr. W. Winter, who bore some kind of grudge against the Infirmary, let off steam by trampling on the rhubarb in the garden. Then on the 19th August, 1891 we read that:

> *"A vote of thanks be passed to Mr. Rowland Brown for the successful way he conducted the case of the garden prosecution against Mr. Winter."*[4]

On the other hand we find the Committee, in October, 1917, writing to the Prime Minister about the National Insurance Bill then before the House. In 1933 the Committee resolved:

> *"...to cease buying butter from the Cow & Gate Company because they are not subscribers to the Infirmary."*[4]

Every week for, 100 years, the Committee appointed two of their number to act as "Visitors of the Week" to inspect the premises and visit the patients. Their report was entered in the Minutes and their recommendations acted upon the following week. The achievement of high standards of hygiene and treatment depended on the House Surgeon, Matron, nurses and servants who, alone, were on the spot to enforce the rules.

The Minutes reveal that the Committee was commendably zealous in their supervision even before the Infirmary was receiving patients:

14 September 1847	*Proposed by Mr. Brigstocke, seconded by Mr. Job Jones that the House be thoroughly cleansed and washed out and that Mr. Collard get it done.*
25 September 1851	*The medical gentlemen having called the attention of the Committee to the offensive and unhealthy smell arising from the Public Slaughter House, the Committee deem it their duty to represent the matter to the Town Council and earnestly to request that some steps be taken to remedy the evil complained of. The Committee feel deeply convinced that the stench which has for some time pervaded the atmosphere throughout the whole neighbourhood of the said*

	slaughter house is most prejudicial to the public health and especially to the inmates of this Infirmary.
5 May 1852	*Visitors report that the yard was often dirty and a privy overflowed. Ordered that the Porter clean it up.*
12 October 1853	*Rev. Dr. Lloyd reported that the smell in the Male Ward was so bad that he could not remain a minute in the room. This offensive exhalation was attributable to the circumstance of a patient drawing his urine. Resolved that, in future, only the House Surgeon or his pupil draw the patient's urine and cause the same forthwith to be removed.*
13 December 1854	*Everything going on orderly*
17 January 1855	*Complaint was made by Mrs. Thomas, Matron of insolence on the part of the patients.*
24 January 1855	*Re. Dr. Lloyd and Rev. A.H. Jones reported that they had reprimanded the patients who had been insolent to the Matron as stated at the last meeting and that the patients expressed their sorrow for their conduct and promised amendment.*
28 January 1855	*Mr. Bagnall reported that there*

	was a slight smell of stale tobacco smoke in the wards and stairs on 8th inst. and he had cautioned the patients.
14 February 1855	*John Evans guilty of smoking tobacco and had been abusive be discharged forthwith provided the surgeon in attendance shall see no objection. His Governor be written to.*

These examples indicate the assiduity with which the House Committee discharged their responsibilities.[4] They resolved to style themselves "Management Committee" in 1935.

The Annual General Meetings were held in April each year and reported in the Carmarthen newspapers. A report was read by the Chairman of the House Committee and proposed changes in the Rules ratified. The 1870s opened with complaints about the *"formal and useless character"* of the meetings. In April, 1870 the **Welshman** reported that:

> *"It was not thought worthwhile to attend a meeting to pass formal resolutions of thanks couched in the same terms from year to year."*[6]

The Vicar of St. Peter's Parish, The Rev. D. Latimer Maurice Jones remarked in the same year that it would be difficult to conceive of a more hopeless failure than the meetings of the past few years. He wanted, despite the conventions of the time which prohibited ladies from taking part in public affairs, to have them at meetings. This broad-minded cleric pointed out that:

> *"…not only would they brighten the proceedings ....but we are constantly in need of linen and lint – some ladies send us some but the great majority nothing at all."*[2]

This remarkable clergyman, who died in 1878, was many years ahead of his time. It was not until 1896 that the first woman was appointed to the House Committee (Mrs. White) and on the 12th October 1912 we learn that permission was given to Matron to try and establish *"a Linen League in connection with the hospital."* In April, 1914 the House Committee announced that the *"Ladies Linen Guild"* under the aegis of Lady Owen Philipps of Cwmgwili has:

> *"...practically relieved the Infirmary of the necessity of providing its linen goods."*[5]

The War made other claims on the time of the ladies concerned and the *"Guild"* lapsed for the duration. At the end of the War Lady Philipps reassumed the Presidency and the organization flourished until the "appointed day". Other luminaries associated with the Guild were Lady Kylsant, Viscountess Deerhurst and Lady Dynevor.

It was the responsibility of the House Committee to vet patients and decide whether the Rules permitted their admission. The whole question is obviously bound up with the problem of providing for their maintenance. All the major changes in policy relating to the admission of patients were brought about for two reasons: firstly, a perpetual shortage of funds and then secondly, a gradual realization that advances in medical science were making hospital treatment beneficial to a much greater number of people.

The original Rules were quite specific about which patients the House Committee should regard as

> *"...suitable objects for charity."*

Those drawn up in 1847 stated that:

> *"No patient shall be admitted or assisted with advice, medicine or bath who are able to subsist themselves or pay for the relief afforded."*[1]

This raised the obvious problem of potential abuse. Thus Wednesday became admissions day when prospective patients would arrive at 11 o'clock with their *"tickets of recommendation"* from their Governor (paid-up subscriber) and enquiry would be made into the means of each applicant. An amusing altercation took place at the Annual General Meeting in 1877 between the Chairman, The Rev. Latimer Jones and another member of the House Committee Dr. Lloyd:

"Dr. Lloyd:	*Patients earning 30 to 35 shillings per week ought not to get relief – it would be downright robbery of the institution. It was only last Tuesday I objected to this without effect.*
Rev Latimer Jones:	*You objected after the patient left the room and then I called her back.*
Dr. Lloyd:	*Of course, I did not think it right to make personal remarks in the patient's presence. But I protest against it now. It is an abuse of the charity to relieve those who can pay for it.*
Rev Latimer Jones:	*I quite agree with you but it has not yet been done.*
Dr. Lloyd:	*I know her circumstances better than you do – indeed it is only recently that she paid me a bill.*
Rev Latimer Jones:	*That's exactly what she said and added that you had nearly ruined her.*

(Loud laughter amidst which Dr. Lloyd resumed his seat)"[2]

If approved by the Committee, which always included one of the

Honorary Medical Staff, the patients were handed on to the House Surgeon as either inpatients or outpatients. The House Surgeon would make appointments for difficult or interesting cases to be seen by his seniors. Out-patients were to attend at the Infirmary:

> *"...punctually at the time appointed by the medical officers. If they neglect to attend to the directions given to them by the medical officers or omit to attend at the appointed time they will be subject to dismissal."*[1]

No fresh medicines were to be given until they:

> *"...return all phials, gallipots and other things they may have been supplied with."*[1]

Each individual was expected to bring with him *"at least 2 shirts or shifts."* If the patient lived some distance from the Infirmary the person recommending him was requested to:

> *"...send beforehand, post paid, a short statement of his case drawn up by his medical attendant."*[1]

so that the Committee could decide whether or when he could be admitted. The House Committee pointed out, however, that they were at liberty to reject a patient if they thought a case had been misrepresented. Letters, signed by the Chairman were sent to subscribers whose *"recommendations"* were rejected explaining the circumstances and also when a patient was discharged.

It was the custom for employers to pay part of the wages of their servants in kind by providing board and lodging. It wasn't intended that the Rules of the Infirmary should exclude domestic or other servants from the benefits of treatment. The Infirmary provided that if a master wanted to send his servant to the Infirmary, and the doctors agreed to admit him, he (the master) should pay one shilling per day towards the board and medical expenses of his servant. The amount was reduced to sixpence per day at the first Annual General Meeting. It was only costing about 3s. 6d. per week to maintain and treat each patient. At the

Annual General Meeting in 1865 the Rule caused a furore that well illustrates that even physicians were unappreciative of the slowly changing role of the voluntary hospitals. They were still regarded as a dreaded last resort, preferable to the Workhouse, but not as a curative establishment. Dr. T. Lewis, who became a physician to the Infirmary in 1873 proposed that the Rule should be rescinded because:

> *"Its presence amongst the regulations of a purely charitable institution was like the fly in the Apothecary's ointment causing it to send forth a disagreeable odour. To make a fixed charge 6d. per day is to convert the sweetness of divine charity into a paltry commercial transaction."*[2]

The Rev. Latimer Jones, a shrewd, fiery and practical character, with uncanny prescience, who sat on most Committees in the town and appears to have made a tremendous impact during his incumbency of the Parish of St. Peter from 1863 to 1878 (the Lych Gate and oak pulpit of St. Peter's Church were erected in his memory), was:

> *"…at a loss to see what hardship or disgrace there was in a master paying 6d. a day for the maintenance of his servant. It certainly secures to the master a most gracious mode of acknowledging the assistance the Infirmary gave to such a patient. Besides the 6d. might be evaded by anyone roguish enough to do so by means of giving the servant permission to absent himself from service until restored to health."*[2]

He failed to see any good reason for rescinding the Rule and strongly opposed the motion. However, Dr. Lewis won the day and it was another 20 years before the House Committee realized that progress and medical skill and nursing care meant that the Infirmary was no longer just a "charity" but was in a position to provide an important and necessary service to all classes of society.

In 1847 only:

> *"…urgent cases which admit of no delay."*[1]

were admitted without the recommendation of the President, a Vice-President or Governor:

> *"...in which case the House Surgeon or Matron shall receive the patient giving immediate notice to the physician or surgeon of the week and reporting the circumstances to the next weekly Committee."*[1]

The view of the Honorary Medical Staff and Committee would not always coincide with that of the House Surgeon or Matron when an *"urgent"* case came up for review. The latter would, understandably, be reluctant to incur the displeasure of their employer. Thus many acutely ill persons would have been kept out until the next admissions day who might well have benefited from more prompt diagnosis and treatment.

The Infirmary would:

> *"...admit no woman big with child, no person disordered in their senses, or who have smallpox, epilepsy, itch or any infectious distemper, nor any person who is apprehended to be in a dying or consumptive state or who may receive equal benefit as an out-patient."*[1]

A creditable turnover of cured patients was important for "Appeal" purposes. When there shall be:

> *"...want of room in the Infirmary for duly recommended and qualified in-patients preference shall be given, firstly, to cases of greatest urgency, secondly, to those that live at the greatest distance and thirdly, to those recommended by those subscribers who have not recommended any in-door patients for the greatest length of time."*[1]

There was another rather sinister rule relating to in-patients which stipulated that all subscribers recommending a patient:

> *"...must deposit with the Secretary, one guinea, as security for the expense of the funeral if the patient die or his*

> *journey home if cured. In the case of the money not being required for these purposes it will be returned to the person recommending."*[1]

The subscribers "ticket" system caused many difficulties particularly in hospitals where the medical staff was not represented on the Committee which vetted each patient. The medical men would want to admit patients whose swift recoveries would attest to the efficacy of their skill and care. It was quite likely that persons whom subscribers thought worthy of their charity would turn out to be chronic or incurable cases that would "block" the bed indefinitely. Moreover, many subscribers expected their nominee to be admitted for the full term of their "ticket" which was usually six to eight weeks. The only record of any dispute between the doctors and the lay Committee members, was with regard to eligibility and relates to the period 1930 to 1933 and the details are not clear. The medical staff was, in fact, well-represented on the Committee and when difficulties did arise usually had its way. In 1847 the Carmarthenshire doctors had clearly envisioned the possibility of blocked beds for they included the following Rule:

> *"All persons, who within 2 months, receive no true benefit shall be discharged unless the medical officer, after due consultation, certifies to the weekly Committee that there is a probability of cure or considerable relief."*[1]

The Minutes show that the Committee regularly invoked this Rule when beds became in short supply.

TRADITIONAL METHODS OF FUND RAISING

There was one impediment to the work of every voluntary hospital – a perpetual shortage of funds because of the rising cost of living. Later on, as treatment became more complex and thus expensive, all sorts of schemes were devised to ensure a regular income for the Infirmary. In the early years, apart from subscriptions, funds were raised by holding bazaars, fetes, charity balls, concerts, eisteddfods, converzaziones, dinners, Miles of Pennies, Alexandra Rose Days, Infirmary Saturdays and by collecting legacies and donations from all classes. The initial subscription list was steadily depleted by death, removal from the area and waning of interest. In order to stimulate support and enlist new residents the town and surrounding district was regularly canvassed by volunteers. In 1881, Major the Count de Kantzow said that:

> *"...when he came to the town some years ago he had the honour of being waited upon by their worthy Secretary before he was 48 hours a resident."*[2]

The very first elaborate fund raising function was advertised by the Carmarthen Journal on the 7th July, 1848:

Carmarthenshire Infirmary Bazaar
Under the Patronage of

The Countess of Cawdor	*Lady Lucy Foley*
Lady Dynevor	*Lady Mary Williams*
Viscountess Emlyn	*Lady Griffiths Williams*
Lady Milford	*Lady Mansel*
The Hon. Mrs. Rice-Trevor	*Mrs. Saunders-Davies*

The Fancy Bazaar

In aid of the funds of the Carmarthenshire Infirmary will be held in the New Market Place on Thursday the 20th July instant and continue open on the Friday and Saturday following commencing each day at 12 o'clock

The Ball

In aid of the same benevolent object will take place at the Boars Head Assembly Rooms on Saturday the 22 July instant

Tickets

Gentlemen 10s. 6d. *Ladies 7s. 6d.*

The Journal reported the events in, delightfully, archaic style:

> *"At 12 o'clock the Bazaar was opened and an opportunity thus afforded of seeing the handiwork of the Ladies of this and other Counties and a truly magnificent site it was far surpassing, we are sure, what even the most sanguine could reasonably have expected. The Bazaar was held in the Cooper's Shed of the New Market and was excluded from the public gaze by a boarding which is carried up sufficiently high to prevent those who decline to pay the admission fee from having the least view of the magnificent site within. The shed is very elegantly fitted up, the walls are covered with drapery of various colours and prettily festooned with evergreens and flowers....from the roof are suspended numerous wreaths and garlands very tastefully arranged. One part of the shed including the clerk's office is boarded off for the express use of ladies. To the right a species of orchestra has been formed for the Amateur Brass Band who, throughout the day, discoursed eloquently sweet music. It is to be regretted that none of the Lady Patronesses were present."*[2]

The Bazaar made £332 17s. 6d. and the Ball £14 13s. 0d.

On the 11th December, 1851 the House Committee ordered that *"the offer of H. Brinley Richards to assist in rendering his services at a concert for the benefit of the Infirmary be thankfully accepted."* The Secretary was asked to write to H. Brinley Richards *"to insure the pianoforte to be sent for the concert to and fro the expense to be defrayed by the Infirmary Committee."* The **Welshman** announced that Mr. Richards, who was a Professor at the Royal Academy of Music, would be assisted by the Carmarthen Musical Society and *"several distinguished amateurs."* The programme was to include several of his own compositions which include "God bless the Prince of Wales".

The concert was held at the Shire Hall on the 11th February, 1852:

"Tickets at 3/6 each

Entrance – At the Side Door

Carriages to set down and take up with horses' heads towards General Nott's Monument."[6]

A reporter from the **Welshman** was in the audience:

> *"Expectation had been so long on the 'qui vive' with regard to this musical demonstration that we were not in the least surprised to find the doors of the Shire Hall literally besieged with applicants the instant ingress was afforded. The sub-committee were indefatigable in their intentions and endeavours to provide all with comfortable seats but, notwithstanding this, Viscount Emlyn, the Mayor, Baron de Rutzen Franz and a great many other gentlemen were compelled to stand during the greater part of the performance. The concert with 50 performers was such a success that Mr. Brinley Richards was requested to stay and give a second performance for the benefit of the Infirmary fund and at great personal inconvenience he consented."*[6]

Total receipts were £77 2s. and net profit £51 17s. 1d.

This tradition survived the extinction of the voluntary hospitals. The League of Friends of the West Wales General Hospital still raises money in this way to provide amenities for both patients and staff.

For most of its existence the Infirmary operated with a deficit on its current account ranging from a few pounds to a few thousand pounds. But as the Vicar of St. Peter's Church, the Rev. Latimer Jones pointed out in 1869 whilst trying to placate anxious subscribers (current account deficit - £22 10s. 6d.):

> *"Some people look with a sort of holy awe at an adverse balance but I have never known them to do any harm."*[2]

Indeed, some crafty Treasurers deliberately obtained a debit balance on their current accounts by transferring revenue to their capital accounts thereby hoping to encourage subscriptions.

SUBSCRIPTION PROBLEMS

In 1871 the annual cost of food and medicine was £488 for 24 patients – the higher than average daily number accommodated that year. Thus each patient was costing about £20 per year. As there was only a small deficit it was pointed out that an addition of £120 to £150 to the subscription list would enable them to take in the full complement of 30 patients. Because of the shortage of beds admissions were often delayed until beds became empty. The Rev. Latimer Jones thought that part of the blame for this state of affairs should be ascribed to the people of Llanelly:

> *"They ought to do a great deal more for us. They do a great deal in one way, they send a number of interesting cases – patients with very curious diseases and accidents of all kinds which serve as excellent studies for the medical men and the Infirmary is thankful for them. But the thankfulness would be much increased if the Llanelly people sent a little more money to keep the Infirmary going. Some years ago they helped the Infirmary a great deal but lately they have been talking about their Village Hospital and their love for the Infirmary has grown cooler. They take from the Infirmary about £100 and give back only £20."*[2]

It was then arranged to organize a meeting to:

> *"...induce the good people of Llanelly to subscribe."*

The Committee also directed that the Secretary should:

> *"...annually solicit the Vicar of St. Peter's, the several clergymen and Ministers of the different Meeting Houses*

> *for religious worship in this town and county to preach a sermon once in each year and use their best endeavours with their respective congregations to promote collections for the benefit of the institution."*[4]

The clergymen and ministers were encouraged to do this, as might be expected, by offering them the same power of recommending patients as persons subscribing the same amount.

EMPLOYERS AND PUBLIC AUTHORITIES

As well as individual subscribers being able to recommend patients it was provided that:

> *"The Head Officer of any Parish or District or the Head Officer of any Society or Public Company shall have the same power of recommending patients with a subscriber or benefactor of equal value. The Executor, or Executors jointly, of any person leaving a legacy to the Infirmary and the person charged with a benefaction from an unknown hand have the same privileges of recommending patients as if they themselves had given the benefaction."*[1]

The Carmarthen Union began its subscription immediately after it was empowered to do so by the Poor Law Amendment Act of 1851 and a member of the Board of Guardians became a Governor. No doubt the Guardians considered this an appropriate and inexpensive solution to the problem of providing a proper hospital for the acutely sick in the Workhouse. The voluntary hospitals, of course, used the Workhouses as dumps for their chronics, incurables and lunatics. The Board of Guardians in Carmarthen never did trouble to provide a separate Infirmary although, as already mentioned, there was an area in the building known as the *"sick ward"*. There were no trained staff at Penlan until the Second World War apart from the period during the Great War, 1914 to 1918, when the institution was taken over by the Red Cross and staffed, primarily, by the Infirmary. The Penlan Workhouse came under the authority of the County Council under the

Local Government Act, 1929. It continued to provide accommodation for the elderly, disabled and chronic sick. On the outbreak of the Second World War Penlan opened 30 acute and 10 Maternity beds for convalescent patients (all the operative Obstetrics was performed at the Infirmary) and recruited trained nurses to staff them. These beds were temporarily used for casualties from the Swansea blitz in February, 1941.

Under the Poor Laws the Infirmary was not prepared to have more than one Guardian on the House Committee – the Chaplain. There were often *"matters in dispute"* with the Guardians and:

> *"...there is no depending which side he would take."*[4]

Moreover, pauper patients were:

> *"...third class citizens, despised and disenfranchised."*[4]

and anybody connected with the Poor Law, apart from people like the Chaplain, tended to be ostracized by polite society. Other Unions also paid annual subscriptions to the Carmarthen Infirmary, among them, Llanelly, Llandeilo, Llandovery and Narberth. The Committee then ordered that:

> *"In future no pauper in receipt of parochial relief be admitted as an indoor or outdoor patient unless recommended by the Clerk of the Union to which he belongs."*

When the Bishop of St. David's moved the first resolution at the meeting on the 17th October, 1846 he stressed that:

> *"...the already urgent need for an Infirmary would be considerably aggravated when the great public works now about to be commenced in the County are in active progress from the increased number of accidents which may, naturally, be expected to occur during their prosecution."*[2]

He was referring to the building of the London – South Wales Railway which reached Carmarthen in 1852. That the *"Head Officers of Public Companies"* were slow or reluctant to insure their employees against accidents is evidenced by an entry in the Minutes on the 27th July, 1853 which, whilst resolving that:

> *"all accidents of whatever nature are at all times admissible to the Infirmary."*[4]

directed that the Secretary should communicate the resolution to the Proprietors of Works and solicit contributions to the funds.

PRIVATE PATIENTS

In April, 1886 at the Annual General Meeting a decision was taken which was to mark the beginning of a gradual metamorphosis in the whole character of the institution. For the first time in Carmarthenshire it was conceded that, in certain circumstances, the indisposed well-to-do might have a better chance of recovery in the Infirmary than in their own homes and would also be a source of income for the Infirmary. Some of the credit for this important decision must be given to Mr. W. J. Morgan, owner of the **Welshman** newspaper and a member of the House Committee, who moved that the rules should be altered to permit the admission of fee-paying patients:

> *"For the past year patients had been admitted to undergo serious operations because of the far better nursing they would receive than in their own homes and because of the promptitude with which they could be attended to if anything went wrong."*[6]

It will be recalled that a decision had been made to employ a trained Matron at the previous Annual General Meeting. In support of his motion Mr. Morgan cited the case of a rich farmer who had been involved in a serious accident and the Committee, having a vacant room, allowed him to be treated. Mr. Morgan said that:

> *"No doubt his life would have been sacrificed but for the care and attention bestowed upon him at the Infirmary."*[6]

Apparently, whilst in the Infirmary he had promised a substantial donation but:

> *"...we did not receive a single farthing from him."*[6]

There had been several similar instances. John Hughes, F.R.C.S. thought it should be made as easy as possible for fee-paying patients to be admitted:

> *"No one should be put to the degradation of saying to a subscriber 'I want to go to the Infirmary'. If the institution fills up we can always turn out the fee-paying patients. We have room for 40 in-patients in the House and if we have 20 who pay it will be easier to maintain the rest. The Infirmary would benefit considerably."*[6]

It was reassuringly pointed out that Swansea already had such an arrangement.

The Rule was amended to read:

> *"No persons shall be admitted for advice or bath who can pay for the relief afforded them, but any such person may, on the approval of the Committee, and only on the recommendation of the medical staff in chronic cases, be admitted to all the benefits of the institution on payment of from one to four guineas in advance and such persons shall be subject to the same laws as other patients."*[1]

The question of depriving local doctors of their livelihood did not arise because the Infirmary was, more or less, controlled by doctors who were local practitioners. Each case was treated on its merits and an additional fee charged by the medical men for their professional services. However, the rich showed very little inclination to take advantage of the new rule and there was never more than, perhaps, a dozen such patients admitted in any one year and these were, invariably, accident cases. The payments derived from such patients amounted to less than 1% of the total income for many years. Dr. F. Oppert devotes a paragraph of his book to the provision of *"small wards"* and the attitude of the period is summed up as follows:

> *"Persons who belong to the better class of society but have become hospital inmates by accident, feel thankful if they are removed to a side-ward where they are alone, or only with one or two others."*[7]

There was only one *"side-ward"* at the Infirmary" until the Nurses' Hostel was opened in 1922.

WORKMEN'S COLLECTIONS

For the less well-off a rather haphazard "insurance" system had evolved since 1876 when Mr. Howell Howells, the Secretary, had suggested that:

> *"Working men in factories and other establishments should be given a chance to contribute, perhaps, weekly to the funds. Their employers are already subscribers and they would certainly feel more independent if they had to be admitted as the result of an accident or some other misfortune."*[5]

This was agreed to by the Governors and the first to take advantage of the scheme were local employees of the Great Western Railway Company and the Tin Works. The Infirmary was keen to organize regular collections from workers and, in 1895, instituted a formal "Hospital Saturday" collection but the idea never really caught on.

The administrative difficulties of organizing the collections were one obstacle even though, after 1907, the newly-formed Boy Scout movement lent a hand. The trouble was that the Committee were not prepared to concede that contributors to such schemes had a moral or legal right to treatment either for their dependents or themselves. The benefits they received were regarded as being essentially privileges and patients had to be properly recommended by their nominated Governor. The workmen's representatives were only permitted the same privileges as subscribers of a similar amount. Any other arrangement, the Committee thought, would have resulted in an Outpatient Department crammed with applicants who could, and should, have resorted to their general practitioner. This would be "abuse" of the charity. The Minutes record frequent acrimonious disputes, between those who had contributed to the schemes and the Committee, about the rights of the respective parties. The income from this source was less than 6% of the total until a contributory scheme was formalized in 1926.

The Infirmary struggled on during the latter part of the nineteenth century and the early part of the twentieth by juggling between the various accounts (capital, revenue, improvement, nursing etc.) and relying on the generosity of supporters to wipe out debt. Despite the difficulties the Committee were strongly opposed to any form of State aid. An entry in the Minutes in 1892 resolves that:

> *"We co-operate with Sheffield in opposing the Bill now before Parliament to enable Municipal Corporations and other Local Authorities to give grants from the rates, if they think fit, in aid of Infirmaries and suchlike charitable bodies supported by voluntary contributions and to ask Mr. Sanford of Sheffield to forward a petition for signature – on condition that we incur no expense. Also that the Secretary write to the County and Borough M.P.s asking them to oppose the Bill in Parliament."*[4]

The reasons for this strong opposition will become clearer as we trace the story.

NATIONAL INSURANCE

As a result of the Royal Commission on the Poor Laws of 1909 and the enthusiasm of Mr. David Lloyd-George, a Welshman and Chancellor of the Exchequer, the National Insurance Bill was passed in 1911 and became law on the 13th January, 1913. Under the Act manual workers and all others with incomes below £160, between the ages of 16 and 70, were required to pay 4d. per week to an approved society. This meant a "Friendly Society" or "Provident Club" approved by the Insurance Commissioners. Employers were required to pay 3d. and the State 2d. This entitled the insured person to a "panel doctor", a limited sickness benefit and the supply of drugs and medicines. The Clubs were not empowered to pay the voluntary hospitals for the treatment of insured persons. On the 30th July, 1912 a letter was dispatched to the House Committee by the Honorary Medical Staff:

> *To the Chairman and Members of the House Committee of the Carmarthenshire Infirmary*
>
> *Mrs. Lister and Gentlemen,*
>
> *We, the undersigned beg to inform you that we have been advised to notify the Committee of Management of the Carmarthenshire Infirmary that, having signed the pledge of the British Medical Association, we will be compelled on and after January 13th 1913 to decline to render service to any insured person except in cases of urgent necessity unless terms satisfactory to the British Medical Association are first conceded by the Insurance Commissioners.*[5]
> *Yours faithfully,*
>
> *Ll. M. Bowen Jones*
> *R. G. Price*
> *E. R. Williams*
> *C. P. Parry*
> *J. Fraser*

This letter from the doctors implied that the class of person for whom the Infirmary was founded was no longer eligible for treatment.

Furthermore, there was much anxiety expressed about the possibility of a decline in voluntary support. To counter the belief that the Infirmary was no longer necessary now that patients had a "panel doctor" the Committee issued a 5 point appeal:

1. *In the whole country only 50% of those treated in hospitals are insured persons and in Carmarthen and District only 25% are insured.*

2. *The work for which hospitals exist is the treatment of serious accidents, acute diseases and surgical operations which cannot be attended to in the homes of the people, all of which require skilled nursing.*

3. *Hospitals are the only places where nurses can be effectively trained.*

4. *The treatment of insured persons under the Act is only such as can be given to the sick in their own homes by an ordinary general practitioner.*

5. *The most important part of hospital work which is the treatment of inpatients remains unaltered and as the greater number of outpatients are uninsured persons the work of the Outpatients Department is little affected by the Act.*[5]

If the doctors continued to refuse to treat insured persons the Government would have been forced to consider some form of State control. In 1911 the voluntary hospitals were providing a total of 43,000 beds out of a national total in both public and private sectors of 197,000. This amounted to 5.5 unevenly distributed beds per 1000 of the population of the United Kingdom of approximately 36,000,000. The population of Carmarthenshire, then as now, was estimated to be approximately 180,000. In Carmarthen all beds for acute cases were provided by the Infirmary. The doctors and the Committee men, in common with their colleagues all over the country wanted the Infirmary to be paid for looking after insured patients but without interference from the State. If the Approved Societies were permitted to make donations to hospital funds insured patients would have demanded free treatment and the whole system of voluntary support would be undermined. It would also have meant official interference and neither the Government nor the British Hospitals Association (the Act had the effect of uniting the Managers of the voluntary hospitals for the first time), now the spokesman for the voluntary hospitals, wanted to see the extinction of the movement. The matter was left in abeyance until an emergency meeting of the House Committee (including the ex-officio members – the doctors) decided to compromise on the very day the Act became law.

Medical treatment of insured persons would cease forthwith:

> *"...except with the express sanction of the Committee under very special circumstances."*[4]

Urgent surgical cases were to be treated as before but were to be:

> *"...referred to their medical man as soon as may be possible."*[4]

A record was to be kept of any insured persons applying for treatment – whether treated or not. If an insured person was to be found without a "panel" doctor and required inpatient accommodation he had to sign a form authorizing his society to pay over his sickness benefit to the Infirmary. People who were already contributing to one of the "collecting schemes" objected strongly if they were referred to their panel doctors or refused treatment – another reason for the five point appeal.

The Honorary Medical Staff were not unduly concerned by the refusal of the Insurance Commissioners to grant some form of pro rata payments. Firstly, it meant that they were not subject to any form of control or under any obligation to an official body. Secondly, as general practitioners, they were also "panel" doctors and assured of a regular and generous income. Thirdly, by virtue of their Infirmary appointment they were the "top" doctors of the area and had lucrative private practices. It has been estimated that it would require a 400%

pay-rise to restore the relative earning power of the present day full-time NHS Consultant to that of his predecessor before the National Health Service was established. The main tendency of the Act, as far as the Infirmary was concerned, was to exclude the more trivial cases and to re-establish it on a more consultative basis. It obviously paid the "panel" doctor to refer his more worrying surgical cases to the Infirmary where they were treated free of charge. The appointment of Mr. W. F. Brooks as the very first "specialist" on the 17th September, 1913 confirms this conclusion. A tendency was also established, at this time, for the Honorary Medical Staff to specialize and, as already pointed out, many of them became Consultants in their particular interest in the National Health Service on the 5th July, 1948.

THE GREAT WAR - 1914 to 1918

The outbreak of war on the 4th August, 1914 had tremendous repercussions throughout the hospital world and throughout every hospital department, not least affecting a financial situation which was, at least initially, *"transformed from one of bare solvency to one of relative affluence."* In 1899, an offer of 8 beds for wounded soldiers from the Boer War had been made to the War Office although they had not been used. On the day hostilities were declared the House Committee, in an ardour of patriotism, dispatched another letter to the War Office making a similar offer of:

> *"...12 beds with the necessary medical and hospital accommodation for the sick and wounded during the present war and assured the War Office that, if necessary, every empty ward will be available for the purpose."*[5]

It is extremely unlikely that the Committee were aware that the War Office intended to pay for the maintenance of each soldier admitted so this was a generous offer. However, the War Office advised the Committee that it had:

> *"...asked the Red Cross to investigate and advise on all*

> *offers of accommodation and to act as co-coordinating agent for these auxiliary hospital units."*[5]

The British Red Cross Society was a fashionable and powerful organization and during the War, raised and spent £21 million. No one had expected a lengthy war or heavy casualties and the plans that had been laid proved to be quite inadequate. The Red Cross, with its own funds but on behalf of the Government, established auxiliary hospitals all over the country including one of 60 beds at the Penlan Workhouse in Carmarthen. Many of the pauper lunatics were shunted off to the Joint Counties Lunatic Asylum which had been renamed St. David's Hospital.

After receiving the reply from the War Office to the House Committee's letter Canon Brown addressed himself to the Chairman of the Carmarthen Branch of the British Red Cross Society – Dame Margaret Pryse-Rice:

> *Dear Mrs. Pryse-Rice,* *20th August, 1914*
>
> *I am directed by the Committee of the Carmarthenshire Infirmary to inform you that a letter has been received from the War Office stating "we are prevented under Field Service Regulations from accepting offers of voluntary aid except through the British Red Cross Society." The Committee, therefore, makes the following offer to the Red Cross Society:*
>
> *To reserve 12 beds for wounded men and, if accommodation can be found to admit other wounded soldiers.*
>
> *To allow its outdoor staff of trained nurses, 4 in number to offer their services to the Red Cross for nursing outside the Infirmary. The offer on the part of the nurses is to be regarded as purely voluntary.*
>
> *The Carmarthenshire Infirmary may be used by the Red*

Cross Society as a depot for receiving and distributing surgical and other necessaries, it being understood that the Infirmary shall not be responsible for their purchase.

The Board Room of the Infirmary may be used for meetings of the Red Cross Society.

The Matron is to lend, if necessary, such domestic utensils as are not required at the Infirmary itself.

The Infirmary Committee wishes it to be clearly understood that, as its staff of Resident Medical Officer, nurses and servants is necessary for the efficient working of the Infirmary it cannot see how that staff can be reduced in times of special difficulty.

It seems, however, that the services of the Matron have been, in a measure, pledged to the Red Cross Society and that the work of the Society will be hampered should those services not be rendered. The Committee, therefore, agrees that the Matron shall carry out the duties she has promised to perform provided that the efficiency of the Infirmary is not impeded thereby.[5]

Yours faithfully,

C.G. Brown

The offer was gratefully accepted and an association between the Infirmary and the local Red Cross Society began, and continued, to the benefit of both parties. In February, 1917 an agreement was concluded between H.M. Explosives Works, Pembrey and the Infirmary placing 8 beds at the disposal of the former at a retaining fee of £26 5s. per annum and at a weekly charge of £1 5s. 0d. per patient. In June, 1918 the Ministry of Pensions, responsible for discharged servicemen, agreed to pay 5s. per patient per day for a maximum of 12 such patients and 1s. per day for any outpatients it cared to send. It would seem that the principle of fee-paying patients was becoming established. Presenting the House Committee's report, for 1918-19,

Canon Brown reviewed the part played by the Infirmary in the war effort:

> *"The medical staff of the Infirmary has been the medical staff of the Red Cross Hospital at Penlan. Its X-ray Department and its Operating Theatre have been utilized for Red Cross purposes and the nursing staff of the Infirmary has attended to Red Cross patients treated in the Infirmary wards. Our Matron generously volunteered, with the approval of the House Committee, to act without remuneration as the Matron of the Red Cross Hospital and during the war she has, with much sacrifice of time and labour, been Matron of both hospitals with benefit to the one and with no loss of personal influence to the other. The number of soldiers occupying beds at the Infirmary during the war was 39 and the payments made to the Infirmary by the Red Cross Committee amount to £440 11s. 9d. In Carmarthen many soldiers have been billeted and a remount depot has been established. Munitions works have been erected in the County at Pembrey and Carmarthen has been the Centre for soldiers working on the land and women workers on the land. The Infirmary has opened its doors to any of these workers requiring hospital treatment and many have benefited from its hospitality. The Infirmary has been able to do this without restricting the number of beds available to the civilian population and without the slightest inattention to their needs, partly by turning the Committee Room into a ward but chiefly through the devotion of the medical and nursing staff whose cheerful and ready acceptance of the new and onerous conditions by the circumstances of the times the House Committee now gratefully acknowledges."*[5]

How far the ordinary civilian population in Carmarthen was affected by the drafting of their local doctors and by the admission to the Infirmary of military personnel, war workers and, at one time, Belgian refugees, is difficult to determine. Canon Brown was careful to point out that the civilian sick received adequate care. There must have been some decline in the standards of treatment available if only by reason of the extra burdens placed on the medical and nursing staff who had not been conscripted. Only 39 soldiers over 4 years of war is a very small number but, even so, they were the heroes of the hour and for their benefit archaic systems of discipline would have been relaxed to the long term advantage of hospital patients in general.

EFFECTS OF THE FIRST WORLD WAR

The need for the co-ordination of health services was only recognized as trainloads of wounded soldiers began to arrive in England from the Western Front creating chaos amongst the public and private organizations responsible for their care. The rigours of war revealed the weaknesses of the National Insurance Act. There was no cover for dependents and no provision for hospital and specialist facilities and no central supervising body. The lessons learned in the war should have led to reform but there was such a divergence of view about what needed to be done that it needed another World War 20 years later to stir the Government into action. The First World War did result in the establishment of a single Ministry which absorbed the public health work of Local Authorities, housing, health insurance and the whole Poor Law administration. The first Minister was Dr. Christopher Addison the first of only a handful of physicians to hold the post. The range of duties was vast and made it extremely difficult for the Ministry of Health, as it was called, to become an effective administrative unit. The voluntary hospitals, at the end of the war, had come perilously close to complete financial collapse. The new Minister of Health, Sir Alfred Mond, later to become President of the Carmarthenshire Infirmary, set up a Royal Commission chaired by Lord Cave (who became Lord Chancellor in 1922) which reported in 1921 and advised an immediate grant of £1 million to the voluntary hospitals but came out against permanent aid.

> *"The personal relationship between doctor and patient and nurse would be difficult to reproduce under an official regime and the infinite care which is given to the management and support by Boards of Management and*

> *Hospital Aid Societies could hardly be reproduced under State control."*[8]

The Minister decided that £500,000 should be distributed amongst the voluntary hospitals by a Committee appointed to consider each case but also suggested aid from the rates. The House Committee of the Carmarthenshire Infirmary was unanimously opposed to aid of this kind and, on the 8th November, 1920, dispatched a resolution to all local Members of Parliament:

> *This Committee consider it most undesirable that voluntary hospitals shall receive aid from the rates or that Local Authorities shall be enabled to make contributions out of the rates for their benefit."*[5]

They welcomed the unconditional grant but were in for a disappointment. The Distributing Committee, reported Canon Brown:

> *"...had declared that the income of the Carmarthen Infirmary (including free legacies) was in excess of ordinary expenditure for the previous 5 years. How that Committee arrived at that decision or upon what statements it is based is a mystery....there is no such thing as a free legacy to our credit."*[5]

(A "free legacy" was money bequeathed to charity and not liable for death duty).

> *"Our disappointment was all the keener when we learned that the Distributing Committee had made a very generous donation to a German Hospital, solely under German control and open, as is stated, to German patients only"*[5]

The House Committee doggedly pursued the issue and by the end of 1923 had wangled £396 from the grant. The voluntary hospitals had been redeemed and prices began to fall but the managers were faced with new problems.

During the war large numbers of officers from the middle and upper classes, as well as other ranks, were exposed to hospital care. This had the effect of not only emphasizing the advantages of hospitalization in sickness but accustomed a much wider spectrum of social classes to hospital treatment. The question of "abuse" was raised once again. But the House Committee of the Carmarthenshire Infirmary had been much quicker than many of their colleagues in other hospitals to appreciate the potentialities of the changing circumstances. As already mentioned, the principle of charging patients according to their means and insured patients their "weekly" panel money had been initiated in 1913 and formalized in the Rules in January and February, 1916 although enforcement was often lax. At the Annual General Meeting in 1920 Canon Brown summed up the financial position of the voluntary hospitals thus:

> *"We are faced with three possibilities – bankruptcy, nationalisation or requiring patients to pay for their maintenance in hospital according to their means. Should the State be entirely or partly responsible for the maintenance of our hospitals? State aid means State control of hospitals and does not make for hospital efficiency. This was convincingly proved during the late war. Those who had experience of Red Cross Hospitals know how the efforts of those in charge were impeded and their work hampered by official interference and by regulations which were continually being altered and were often contradictory. Carmarthenshire Infirmary has had four years practical experience of such an arrangement whereby after due enquiry as to the patient's means inpatients were required to pay whatever the House Committee decided was an appropriate charge. Nothing is asked or obtained from the poor and those who are unable to pay are as freely admitted to the benefits of the Infirmary as those who are able."*[5]

The House Committee described the task of enquiring into the means of each patient and fixing the charge considered suitable as *"unenviable and invidious."*[5] but were obliged, because of lack of funds, to be extremely diligent in so doing. Then, in 1921, it was announced that per capita payments would be made by Approved Societies towards the cost of an insured patient's maintenance under an amendment to the Insurance Act. In 1922 income tax relief was allowed to persons who covenanted to make payments to a charity for, at least, 6 years. In 1926 the old workmen's collecting scheme which as has been seen caused many problems was converted into a contributory scheme. Mr. Walter Lloyd J.P. announced that:

> *"The men in the offices, sheds and stations at Carmarthen, Ferryside, Whitland and Newcastle Emlyn had agreed to allow a deduction of 2d. per week from their pay. In return we have pledged to give free treatment at the Infirmary to the contributors and their dependents and we admit, at once, that our terms are generous whether too generous only time will tell. It is understood that such a scheme has been adopted by the hospitals in Swansea, Newport and Cardiff and other towns in South Wales."*[5]

In fact, the scheme proved to be a conspicuous success and was soon extended to Asylum workers, miners and others. In 1930, the Road Traffic Act made third party insurance compulsory and insurance companies were compelled, by statute, to pay hospitals for the treatment of road accidents. The strong prejudice which had previously existed against all these sorts of arrangements had been diluted by the benefit the Infirmary had enjoyed from payments for the support of wounded service and other personnel engaged on war work. The medical staff, however, refused to lower their dignity by accepting trifling payments from all the various sources that had arisen. They directed that any "honoraries", to which it was considered they were entitled, be paid into a fund devoted to buying medical and surgical equipment.

Now that people were paying for treatment they expected quality. The fact that their contribution amounted to only a very small proportion of the total cost of their maintenance did not occur to them. There were also the private patients to consider. Professor Abel-Smith quotes "The Hospital" which, in 1922, pointed out that:

> *"Various details of hospital life bore the stamp in the derogatory sense of charity; that the bread is too thick and the mugs are too coarse and the like."*[9]

The complaints began to flood in; the hour at which the patient was awakened; the food; queues in the Outpatient Department etc. The rigours of hospital life had come as no surprise to the old-style patients who were accustomed to hardship but the "better class" of patient now being admitted would not put up with anything that was not comfortable and convenient. In May, 1932 Dr. Alan Trevor Jones had to explain to the Committee that there had been a *"good reason"* for delaying an operation on a " free" patient who had asserted that priority had been given to a private patient.[5] With or without justification there developed a firm belief that there was one class of treatment for patients who paid the doctors and another for the rest.

DEVELOPMENT

This transformation from a "charity" to which poor people reluctantly resorted in time of need to an important service to the community as whole took place between the beginning of the twentieth century and the end of the Second World War. The most important factor was the staggering advance in medical science, catalysed by war, necessitating the purchase, renewal and repair of expensive technical aids to diagnosis and treatment which could be provided only in a hospital. Medical science was becoming so complex that new specialties were rapidly developing to apply the knowledge to clinical medicine and to work the new gadgets. The problem was not as it had been throughout the nineteenth and early twentieth centuries, making income match the rising cost of living, but coping with this huge increase in demand, by providing more beds and expensive treatments.

The House Committee had spent a great deal of money over the years maintaining the building, replacing roof and floors and remodelling as necessary although funds were often provided by wealthy individuals. Mr. Henry Studt, for example, paid for a complete renovation of the Operating Theatre in 1894. An east "sanitary" wing containing laundry, bathrooms, lavatories and mortuary were constructed in 1899 following complaints by the surgeons that their outcomes were poor because of insanitary conditions in their wards. The old drainage pipes and cesspit were removed and the new facilities connected to the Municipal sewer system. A counterpart on the west side was completed in 1904 at a cost of £352. It was decided to *"charge the police"* for the use of the new mortuary at this time.[5]

Wilhelm Roentgen (1845-1923), Professor of Physics in the University of Wurzburg, discovered X-rays almost by accident in 1895. An X-ray apparatus was purchased by the Infirmary in 1911 and, in 1916, some *"additions"* were obtained to *"provide treatment"* for skin malignancies, although how this was controlled is not clear from the record. Advertisements were placed in the local newspapers to try to persuade the public and the local medical practitioners to take advantage of this new service and thus provide a new source of income for the Infirmary. An "Ultra-Violet Ray" apparatus for *"sunlight treatments"* was added to the equipment in 1926 and this was also widely advertised and expected to provide income.[5]

The X-ray machine required an electricity supply and in 1913 it was decided to provide electric light in the Operating Theatre. At this time the Theatre was *"painted white and enamelled"*. The remainder of the building was electrified the following year. Until that time lighting was by means of gas powered *"incandescent burners"* which, in the Operating Theatre, were *"hung from a chandelier"*. A single telephone was installed in March, 1914 the Committee having considered a telephone *"unnecessary"* when the question was first discussed in 1898. *"Rules were drawn up for the use of the instrument."* A telephone switchboard and internal extensions were not provided until 1925. There was a coal fire in each ward and it is recorded that radiators were installed in the corridors in 1924 supplied by a small coal-fired boiler in the basement which was stoked by the Porter. A full central heating system was installed in 1937 and a Boiler House constructed for which the Porter remained responsible. A steam autoclave was also installed at this time and the nurses would pack the autoclave drums with dressings for the porter to sterilise. Instruments continued to be boiled. The coal fire in the Operating Theatre had been replaced with a "Gas Stove" in 1912. Although a *"ream"* of paper and envelopes *"stamped County Infirmary, Carmarthen"* was purchased in 1892 the Infirmary did not possess a typewriter until 1930. A wireless was provided by Sir Alfred Mond in 1925 and, in 1931, this was replaced with an updated "Ediswan All Mains" system with headphones at each bedside and loudspeakers in the Children's Ward. A purpose-built food trolley was obtained in 1931.[5]

A Nurses' Hostel was opened in April, 1922 having cost a total of £14,045 to which the British Red Cross Association contributed £10,000 and £1,500 for endowment using surplus funds which had been raised during the First World War. It was furnished with a donation from *"Mrs. Williams of Llandovery"*. The vacated staff accommodation in the main building was converted, as planned, into wards and the number of beds increased by 15 to 50. The *"...long neglected garden"* behind the hospital was ploughed up, levelled and terraced and as a result *"...we have a suitable recreation ground for convalescing patients and nurses."* The Committee thanked Mr. Morris of Foelewan Farm, Newchurch for *"...his gratuitous work with the plough."*[5]

In October, 1908 the Minutes record that the Committee:

> *"...cannot build an additional ward for children and, therefore, cannot accept the conditional legacy of £500."*[4]

In 1908 the County Council had set up a Schools Medical Service but it is not until 1923 that a *"Children's Ward"* is mentioned in connection with the proposed erection of a *"Balcony or Verandah"* outside it:

> *"...to which beds can be wheeled in the daytime. Open-air treatment is beneficial for tuberculous patients and there are always such in the Children's Ward."*[5]

Accordingly, a "Children's Balcony Fund" was set up and the Balcony completed in 1925 at a cost of £700. A men's ward also opened onto the Balcony so that:

> *"...not only the little tots but adults also may enjoy the maximum of sunshine."*[5]

In fact, a Children's Ward seems to have been designated in 1915 as discussions took place with the County, at that time:

> *"...with regard to the admission of children."*[5]

At the Annual General Meeting held on the 8th March, 1928 it was announced that a new Operating Theatre had been opened at a cost of £290:

> *"...with better lighting and a Scialytique (Shadowless) Lamp, presented by the Ditcham Memorial Committee, has been added to its equipment. Operations numbered 302 which constitutes a record."*[5]

A fund for the provision of an electric lift had been started by Judge Lloyd Morgan in 1924, "*with a handsome donation*", and the lift installed in 1929 at a cost of £700. The balance was raised by the "Mayor's Infirmary Ball Committee.

Henri Becquerel (1852-1908), Pierre Curie (1859-1906) and Marie Curie (1867-1934), working in Paris at the turn of the 19th century, discovered radioactivity and the radioactive elements uranium, radium and polonium. They shared the Nobel Prize for Physics in 1903 and Marie Curie, who was born in Poland, won the Nobel Prize for Chemistry in 1911 for her work on radium. It was Marie Curie who coined the term "radioactivity" and, crucially, realised that radiation was an atomic property of matter the nature of which was elucidated by the New Zealander, Ernest Rutherford (1871-1937) working at the Cavendish Laboratory, Cambridge in the early part of the 20th century. He was awarded the Nobel Prize for Chemistry in 1908. In 1929 we read that:

> *"...88mg of Radium for the treatment of cancer"*[5]

was purchased by the Infirmary from Swansea Hospital for £1,138 17s. 4d. This consisted of:

"...12 Platinum Needles, 4mg each, 2 of 10mg each and 1 of 20mg."[5]

In 1931 it was decided to employ a *"Masseur"*, later to be known as a Physiotherapist, rather than a House Surgeon. *"Electric Sterilizers, an Electric Washer and an Electric Hydro Extractor"* were purchased, in the same year, for the Operating Theatre.[5] Sterilization of surgical instruments was by boiling until the new Theatre suite, in which autoclaves had been installed, was opened at the West Wales General Hospital in the late 1960s.

On the 10th April, 1931 the **Carmarthen Journal** published a leading article entitled *"A Strange Refusal"* following a report that Matron Dorothy Hartland had requested the Carmarthen Branch of the British Red Cross Society to *"remove the society's ambulance, now at Llandovery, to Carmarthen."* Apparently, two separate offers of an ambulance had been refused, only recently, by the Infirmary. The following week an aggrieved response, by the Honorary Secretaries, was published by the Journal. It is worth quoting because it conveys something of the flavour of the time:

"Sir,

Lest your editorial comments in last week's issue of the Journal might prejudice the public mind if allowed to pass unchallenged we feel sure you will be good enough to accord the same publicity to this letter as was given to your own remarks.

You are correct in stating that the offer of an ambulance was declined on two occasions but the refusal was the result of a much more careful and exhaustive consideration than you, unwittingly of course, appear to give the House Committee credit for. They DID face the question from every point of view. Neither did they rely solely on their own judgment but consulted with other hospitals and also sought the opinion of the late Sir Herbert Lewis, Principal Secretary of the Priory of Wales (St. John's Ambulance

Brigade) *than whom it would be difficult to find anyone with more practical and intimate knowledge of the subject.*

Sir Herbert came down to Carmarthen to confer with the Committee and went thoroughly into the details of the matter with the result that he deliberately advised the Committee that it would not benefit the Infirmary to have such an ambulance and gave reasons for his opinion. The question of cost of upkeep was by no means the only difficulty though that would be a much heavier item than the £23 which you state was the total cost to a certain hospital in West Wales.

Sir Herbert strongly deprecated the idea of depending on one of the local garages to provide a driver whenever the ambulance was required. He maintained that every hospital chauffeur should hold a First Aid Certificate so as to be able to deal with every type of injury.

So, far from the employment of a full-time chauffeur being ridiculous as you suggest, the House Committee came to the conclusion that it would indeed be necessary for him to be full-time with more than ordinary driver's qualifications.

As regards the first offer of a motor ambulance which was made by the Carmarthen Motor Cycle and Light Car Club, it must not be supposed the Infirmary suffered loss by the refusal. The Club knew all the circumstances and, as a matter of fact, representatives of the Club were present at the interview between the House Committee and Sir Herbert and the result was that, instead of an ambulance, the Club very generously presented the Infirmary with a new and up-to-date Transformer and X-ray Tube at a cost to the Club of upwards of £200.

The second offer came, as you say, from Mr. E. Walter Rees of Barclay's Bank on behalf of a friend and it was with the utmost regret that the House Committee had to decline this also and for the same reasons as before, which were fully explained to Mr. Rees.

We would point out that accident cases of such a nature as to demand the use of an ambulance are of rare occurrence and ordinary cases can well be transported in comfort by motor cars, which are now plentifully distributed throughout every district in the County and can easily be requisitioned at short notice.

The fact that the ambulance in the West Wales Hospital referred to by you was run so economically seems to imply that there was little demand for its service and that is probably the reason why the Llandovery Hospital Authorities are ready to part with theirs.

The comparison between Aberystwyth and Carmarthen is scarcely relevant. Cardiganshire is sparsely populated and the number of motor vehicles is only about one fourth the number in this County.

In order that there may be no doubt whatever as to what Sir Herbert said we beg to append a letter written on his return to Cardiff after his interview with the House Committee.

We are Sir,
Yours faithfully

J. Richards,
J. Arthur Jones, Hon. Secs. The Infirmary, 14.4.1931"[2]

In fact, it was not until 1945 that the Infirmary accepted, *"with gratitude"* an *"ambulance conveyance from the 'American Ambulance, Great Britain' but as it is only the duty of the Infirmary to give medical and surgical treatment we could not, ourselves, conduct an ambulance service."* The recently-formed volunteer *"Carmarthen*

Ambulance Brigade" based in Francis Terrace had agreed to use the *"'American' ambulance for conveying patients to and from the Infirmary and, in case of need to other places."*[5] In the Annual Report for 1945 the Chairman, Dr. Healy, urged *"all our contributors and supporters to join the Ambulance Scheme and thereby, secure for themselves and their dependents the benefits assured to its members."*[5] In 1947 the Government compelled Counties and County Boroughs to provide ambulance services for their populations. The Carmarthen District Council took over responsibility from the volunteers and ran the service from a small room on the top floor of its offices in Spilman Street. The service has now become highly sophisticated and, since the 1st April, 1998, has been run by the Welsh Ambulance Services NHS Trust which is responsible for the whole principality and employs highly trained Ambulance Technicians and Paramedics. An Air Ambulance service is also provided in partnership with the Welsh Air Ambulance Charity using two modern helicopters. One is based at Swansea Airport and the other in Caernarfon.

We read in the Minutes dated the 24th March, 1925 that a vote of thanks be offered to Dr. Sladden for his Pathology work *"over the years"* and it is also recorded that the first blood transfusions were given in 1927. However, it is not until 1937 that it was agreed to give £20 to Mr. Murphy, laboratory technician, to set up a Pathology Laboratory in an empty nurse's bedroom in the Infirmary *(supported by a Visiting Pathologist from Swansea)*. An *"Iron Lung through the generosity of Lord Nuffield (*William Morris, the motor manufacturer) *and the Radcliffe Infirmary, Oxford,"* was received in 1939. In 1944 a *"complete diathermy plant"* was purchased for the Physiotherapist for £500, *" and, for the kitchen, a heat storage cooker, steaming apparatus and a room for cold storage"*. Interestingly, a rigid gastroscope was purchased in 1946 for £131. 3s. 6d.

EXPANSION

The need for a "Maternity Home" had first been agreed in 1931 and an impetus provided in 1932 when it was learned that the County Council was formulating a scheme to provide maternity accommodation.

Under the Local Government Act of 1929 local authorities (i.e. Carmarthenshire County Council) had became responsible for the Poor Laws bringing the healthcare responsibilities of the Boards of Guardians under the same body as public health services. The Act encouraged the local authorities to develop local hospital services co-ordinating, where necessary with the voluntary hospitals. It was at this time that Workhouse Infirmaries became Municipal Hospitals. They existed throughout the country although not in Carmarthen and many of them survive as NHS hospitals to this day.

An entry in the Minutes on 19 April, 1932 records that:

> *"Llanelly Hospital had already applied for £9,000 to erect a Maternity Hospital – it therefore behoves us to prepare our scheme to submit to the County Council."*[4]

Professor Abel-Smith believes that the practice of obstetrics had developed apart from the mainstream of medicine for two reasons. Firstly, because the College of Surgeons considered it the business of the Physicians who, in turn, considered it beneath their dignity; for example the President of the Royal College of Physicians, in 1827, held that:

> *"Midwifery was an act foreign to the habits of a gentleman of enlarged academic education."*[9]

Secondly, having developed separately in special "Lying-in" Hospitals founded by interested physicians, the danger of infection kept it separate. Bristowe and Holmes recorded that it was continuously observed that puerperal women:

> *"...were highly susceptible to the poison of contagious fevers and sensitive of those conditions on which pyaemia and erysipelas depend."*[10]

The Rule prohibiting the admission of a "*woman big with child*" was regarded as being of critical importance and strictly enforced until well into the twentieth century. For example, on the 17th February, 1858 the Committee ordered that:

> *"The House Surgeon be requested not to attend Mary Jones, an Outpatient residing in Little Water Street on account of its being a Midwifery case."*[4]

On the 14th April, 1876, a Committee Meeting was called to discuss the merits of candidates for the post of House Surgeon one of whom was a Mr. Davies who had a Diploma in Midwifery. The Rev. Latimer Jones felt that the Diploma was:

> *"...a great advantage to Mr. Davies himself but no consequence at all to those connected with the Infirmary which, for excellent reasons, was bound to refuse admission to all patients likely to require Mr. Davies' services in that department of his profession. If a solitary case should occur at rare intervals medical aid could be provided without going to look for men of the skill of Sir James Paget."*[4]

Mr. Davies was not appointed! The Rev. Latimer Jones also objected to the preference some people had for young doctors

> *"...fresh from college, the Infirmary had suffered from being under their management. However minute their theoretical knowledge might be there were few people who, if they were seized with a dangerous illness would not first send for one of the older doctors, one of the most experienced doctors in the neighbourhood. I would certainly do so myself at anyrate."*[4]

Nearly 40 years later, in 1913, there were 107 registered Midwives in Carmarthenshire supervised by the County Medical Officer but no maternity beds at the Infirmary or Penlan and no facilities for "disinfection" provided by the County.[11] The Infirmary agreed, at this time, to help with "disinfection" for a small fee. It was another 20 years before, in 1933, the County Council opened 2 Maternity beds at

Penlan and began exerting pressure on the Infirmary to appoint an Obstetrician who only agreed to appoint Dr. J. R. E. James, in 1936, when the County offered to assist with the cost. 10 Maternity beds at Penlan were opened when war broke out, in 1939, but were temporarily closed during the Battle of Britain so that four 10 bedded wards were available for casualties from the Swansea Blitz. After the Dunkirk evacuation, in May/June, 1940, Penlan admitted about 100 convalescent soldiers.

At this time it was estimated that hospital beds were now one third fewer than required and that, in general, hospitals were in poor repair and ill-equipped. In Carmarthenshire, with its population of 180,000, it was estimated that 450 beds were required on the basis, at the time, of providing a minimum of 2½ beds per thousand of the population. This was a shortfall of 230 beds after the inclusion of the beds in Llanelly. At the Annual General Meeting in 1930 it was announced that a Joint Committee representing Carmarthen Infirmary, Llanelly General Hospital and Llandovery Cottage Hospital had been formed to collaborate with the County Council. Arrangements had already been made with the local authorities for the treatment of children and for specialist and other outpatient services that medical science had made advantageous. In 1913 there were 2 acute hospitals in the County; at Llanelly, the General and Eye Hospital with 40 beds, and at Carmarthen. There was, also, an Isolation Hospital (County Isolation Hospital, Upper Tumble – now Mynydd Mawr Hospital) with 48 beds near Lanelly which was founded in 1903 in a temporary building on the seashore.

The West Wales Sanatorium for Tuberculosis (which became Allt y Mynydd Hospital and closed in 1986) was opened in 1908, by Princess Christian of Schleswig-Holstein (daughter of Queen Victoria), about 3 miles from Llanybyther and had accommodation for 80 patients. 324 cases were notified in 1913.[11] Dr Ll. M. Bowen-Jones, Medical Officer of Health for Carmarthen and Honorary Physician to the Infirmary, was the Secretary and Dr. R. C. Hopkinson was the first "King Edward VII" Tuberculosis Officer. At that time patients were brought to the institution in a pony and trap. An Outpatient T.B. Clinic was opened at 5 Spilman Street in 1912 and was moved into the old Laundry at the

Infirmary in the mid 1940s, to the horror of the staff, and then to a hut on the Glangwili site in the early 1950s. In 1910, deaths in the country from all forms of tuberculosis were 3,600; 1,700 in 1948 and only 368 in 1951. The only other Outpatient Clinic in Carmarthen in 1912 was for Psychiatric patients and it was staffed from St. David's Hospital,

Dr. Alan Trevor Jones made such an interesting and important speech, at a Special Meeting of Ex-Presidents, Vice-Presidents and Trustees on the 25th June, 1934, with regard to the compelling case for an increase in the number of beds and, also for the provision of maternity beds, that it is worth quoting in its entirety:

> *"Firstly, improved transport facilities now make it easier to remove cases from their homes in distant places to the hospital. Secondly, there is less reluctance on the part of patients to submit themselves to hospital treatment. Thirdly, improved methods of diagnosis and treatment have been made available of late; but up-to-date practice requires the use of a well-equipped institution with its operating theatres, X-ray and radium apparatus, pathological laboratory and finally tactful nursing and skilled observation in the ward. These new methods are called for by doctors and patients alike. People have become more conscious of the discoveries of modern research and they demand, and rightly so, the results of this scientific work.*
>
> *These factors which I have mentioned are all on the increase, so that the call on our hospital beds will become even more insistent in the future. I regret to say that the Infirmary is, today, not able to meet with these demands. The overcrowding is a serious problem. Every ward is filled beyond the point which health standards require. Ordinary rooms which were not planned for, nor are satisfactory as wards, are pressed into service to take the overflow of sick and injured persons. There has been, unfortunately, because of this overcrowding the placing together of incompatible types of cases; thus medical cases*

are nursed in the same wards as surgical. This is extremely undesirable both because of the risk of disturbance by one patient of another and also because it makes for lack of efficiency in nursing and treatment. Attendance is not what it might be because of the multiplicity of small wards scattered in various parts of the building and also because of lack of accommodation for nurses.

Furthermore, in the present hospital we are unable to train our own Nurses as we have not the 100 beds required by the Authorities. After one year of probation our young Nurses have to leave the Infirmary to attend another and larger hospital. A training School of our own would be a tremendous advantage and is certainly one of the most important reasons for augmenting the hospital; then we should not lose the services of many loyal and useful nurses. The length of the patients' stay in hospital is often not long enough to satisfy the Medical Staff, and we frequently have to recommend the discharge of patients before they are quite fit to make room for more urgent and serious cases. There is no need to stress the harm of this practice but it is inevitable under the present circumstances.

The need for Maternity beds is most pressing and I think the people of Carmarthen realize this very strongly. At present we have accommodation only for those cases which are obviously abnormal. But I must impress upon you how handicapped the doctor is when he has to deal with these cases in poor and inaccessible surroundings. This is one type of patient to whom we should not refuse to open our doors. There is also a very insistent demand for private wards for many of our patients. As you know there is no Nursing Home in Carmarthen so that the hospital is the only alternative. I need not remind you that the provision of paying beds is a source of profit and income to the hospital.

> *From these points which I have touched upon you will realize that the need for enlarging our hospital is necessary, and I trust that I have made it clear that it will make for increased efficiency also. Hospital services today should rank as highly as any other public service, and all connected with the Infirmary (and I speak particularly for the medical staff) feel that our duty lies clearly, that is, to provide for Carmarthen a bigger and better hospital."*[5]

There was no dissent and it was announced at the Annual General Meeting on the 14th March, 1935 that The Rev. Canon A. W. Parry, M.A., D.Sc., Principal of Trinity College had in 1934 agreed to chair a special Ways and Means Committee dedicated to raising the £30,000 it was estimated would be required. At this meeting, Canon Parry angrily refuted an accusation from an unnamed speaker that the Infirmary was *"cadging"* and railed against the *"discourtesy"* of those who ignored his personal letters soliciting support. On the 25th March, 1937 Canon Parry announced that the foundation stone of the new wing had been laid the previous year by Lady Dynevor and the fund stood at £12,240. The Annual General Meeting in 1935 had approved the design by Mr. Glendinning Moxham, F.R.I.B.A of Cardiff. The main building was to be remodelled thereby increasing the number of beds to 58. The extension would comprise a lower floor-semi basement, corresponding with the existing lower floor, with one 12 bed ward and 5 single rooms, "with the usual offices" for 17 Maternity patients. The Resident Medical Officer's accommodation was also on this floor comprising a self-contained sitting room, bedroom, bathroom and lavatory. The ground floor was to contain one 20 bed Nightingale ward, one 3 bed ward and 4 single rooms. – a total of 27 beds. The grand total of beds would, therefore, be 102. The roof was to be flat, at the level of the first floor of the old building and could be used as a verandah or built over at a later date. The Nurses' Hostel was to be extended by 17 bedrooms with Matron's accommodation being placed on the ground floor in place of the Nurses Dining Room (to be moved into the main building) and adjoining rooms. The laundry was to be taken down as it was on the site of the new block and rebuilt at the far end of the site adjacent to the Parade along with the Mortuary,

Autopsy Room and Boiler House for the new central heating and piped hot water systems. The total cost was estimated at £30,000.[5]

The Committee, however, decided that it was unlikely that such a large sum could be raised from the public and asked Mr. Moxon to modify the plans in order to reduce the cost to not more than £16,000. It was decided not to demolish the Laundry and Mortuary (which was renovated and a small chapel attached to it in 1939) and to avoid the need to remodel the Staff Hostel by purchasing a house on The Parade. Subsequently, further houses in The Parade (numbers 1 to 5) and elsewhere in the town were purchased for staff accommodation. The "hospital" part of the extension was erected as originally planned providing the additional 44 beds. Vacated staff rooms in the main building provided the required 8 beds so the grand total of beds had more than doubled to 102 and the nursing staff had to be increased in number from 15 to 32. The new wards were occupied at the beginning of October, 1937 and formally opened by the Duchess of Kent on the 19th October. She was accompanied by the Duke, brother of King George VI, who asked Canon Parry if he could see the old part of the hospital. The Matron, Miss Hartland overheard and *"whispered to Canon Parry – please say no – it's not been polished up."*[5] Unfortunately, it is not recorded what happened next!

An agreement with the County Council was entered into to:

> *"...provide them with 16 beds and the necessary services in the Maternity ward, while they pay £3. 3s. per bed when occupied and £1 15s. when not occupied. We have also offered 2 beds to the Borough Council on the same terms."*[5]

Maternity patients numbered 73 in 1936 and 458 in 1938, the first full year after the dedicated beds had opened.[5]

Thus the Infirmary not only had had to raise money for the extension but also had to maintain the increased number of beds which had more than doubled. The obvious answer was to increase the scope of the contributory schemes. There was another reason for extending the schemes – there was skulduggery afoot! In July, 1931 Mr. A. Phillips reported that:

> *"Swansea Hospital is making an effort to divert financial support from this Infirmary."*[4]

In January, 1933 it was resolved that:

> *"Mr. Phillips be authorized to counteract those efforts to the best of his ability and to ascertain facts on which we can approach Swansea Hospital re. counteracting their activities."*[4]

In February a local clergyman confirmed that the:

> *"...rumours with regard to Swansea collecting in our district are quite correct."*[4]

When it was announced that *"½ of the people in Llandeilo subscribe to Swansea"* a Captain Nicholas was moved to say that:

> *"They are all Carmarthenshire men and their first duty is to Shir Gar; they must stand by Carmarthen first of all."*[4]

Carmarthen, unlike Swansea, could not afford to employ a paid organizer of collecting campaigns so in 1933 we read that:

> *"The House Committee would be very glad if friends and Governors of the institution in districts were such efforts are being made would confer together as to the best way to counteract them and to rally all support from the area of which the Carmarthenshire Infirmary is the natural centre for hospital purposes."*[5]

It was clear that a solution to both problems was to get the people of the area to join the formal scheme, already in operation for some local employees, which would entitle their dependents and themselves to free treatment on payment of a regular levy. As before there were income limits to protect local practitioners. By April, 1935 some 53 groups had been formed and £1,586 received from 7,000 subscribers. The aim was to encourage all 48,000 people on the electoral roll to subscribe. In 1946, despite the passing of the National Health Service Act and contributors' awareness that their needs were, shortly to be met by the State the scheme raised £7,200 1s. 1d. Each local scheme had its own secretary and vigorous efforts were made to persuade people to join the Carmarthen scheme rather than Swansea's. Mr. J. O. Hill was appointed Honorary Secretary to the whole programme which continued with great success until the "appointed day".[5]

In 1925 the total number of inpatients in the year had topped the 200 mark for the first time in peacetime. This figure rose by leaps and bounds until, in 1940, it had reached 1,634. In 1947, the last year of operation as a voluntary hospital, the number of inpatients was 2,461. The average daily number of inpatients averaged 18 until 1900 when it was 23 but was still only 22 in 1926. It had risen to 48.5 in 1934; 70 in 1940 and 95 in 1947. Outpatients averaged 118 before 1926; 532 in 1934; 977 in 1940 and 7,382 in 1947. Average length of stay had reduced from 42 days throughout the nineteenth century to 22.32 days in 1926 and 15.63 days in 1940 and 13.98 days in 1946. [5]

The average weekly cost of maintaining each patient had risen from 3s. 9½d. in 1851 to only 10s. per week at the end of the nineteenth century. It was £1. 14s. 7d. in 1916 and £3 7s. 4d. in 1926 and was still only £3 6s. 4d. in 1940. At the end of the Second World War, in 1946, it had risen to £6. 5s. 0d. At the end of the nineteenth century total ordinary annual expenditure was about £1,500. In 1916 it had risen to £2,286; in 1932 it was still only £4,252; in 1937 it had doubled to £8,850; in 1940 it was £11,397; in 1943 it had increased to £18,951, in 1946 £32,614 and in 1947 to £43,327. In 1946 the Infirmary treated 2,407 inpatients, 1,219 Casualties, 3,073 X-ray patients, 160 ENT, 570 Eye, 401 Physiotherapy, performed 1,108 operations and dealt with 905 Maternity cases. Average length of stay was 13.98 days per patient.[5]

It is evident from these figures that, although the character of the institution had begun to change with the enactment of the National Insurance Bill and the effects of the First World War the major increase in services and costs took place from the opening of the extension in October, 1937, throughout the Second World War, up to the "appointed day" - 5 July, 1948.

An analysis of the sources of income for the years 1912, 1926 and 1940 is self-explanatory:

Source	1912		1926		1940	
	£		£		£	
Church Collections	139	8.7%	377	13.8%	328	2.9%
Contributory Schemes	0		313	11.6%	4,437	38.9%
Subscriptions/ Donations	409	25.6%	338	12.5%	487	4.3%
Entertainments	171	10.7%	267	9.8%	13	0.1%
Dividends & Interest	539	33.7%	645	23.7%	852	7.4%
Patients' Payments	0		488	17.8%	4,760	41.8%
Miscellaneous (Income Tax rebates, X-ray Charges Home Nursing etc)	54	3.5%	295	10.8%	518	4.6%
Balance due Treasurer (subscriptions)	283	17.8%	0		0	
Total Receipts	£1,595		£2,727		£11,397	

The figures for 1912 have been included because they are typical of the old methods of fund raising with no contributions whatsoever from patients.[5] It is clear that, by 1940, the Infirmary depended on patients' payments and the various contributory schemes for its survival. In the mid-1940s "Private" patients were charged £7. 7s. (7 guineas) per week for a single room and £5. 10s. for a bed on a ward. Maternity patients paid £8. 8s. (8 guineas) for a side-ward and £6. 10s. for a bed on an open ward. Contributors to the funds of the Infirmary were allowed a small discount on these rates.

In 1947 annual expenditure was £43,327 and ordinary income only £18,346. Patients' payments amounted to £5,171 and contributory schemes raised £6,962. Public authority payments in respect of maternity patients, schoolchildren and the Government Emergency Medical Service amounted to £8,262. Fees for the training of midwives totalled £71. The shortfall was made up by the proceeds from the sale of investments - £27,464 and legacies totalling £2,141 leaving a credit balance. Six months later the Infirmary ceased to exist as an independent entity.

References:

[1] Rules & Regulations, County Infirmary, Carmarthen, 1846 & 1857, and subsequent revisions, Carmarthenshire Archives Service.

[2] Carmarthen Journal, 1810 to date (Microfilm), Carmarthen Reference Library.

[3] James J. Healy, M.B. M.Ch., Consulting Ophthalmologist to the County Infirmary, Carmarthen 1921 to 1948 and to the West Wales General Hospital, 1948 to 1957, Chairman of the Management Committee, Carmarthenshire Infirmary, 1st January1946 to 5th July, 1948, Personal communication, 28th April, 1967.

[4] Minute Books, County Infirmary, Carmarthen, 1846 to 1942, Carmarthenshire Archives Service.

[5] Annual Reports, County Infirmary, Carmarthen, 1846 to 1948, Carmarthenshire Archives Service.

[6] The Welshman, 1832 to 1945, (Microfim), Carmarthen Reference Library.

[7] Hospitals, Infirmaries & Dispensaries, F. Oppert, M.D., 1883, British Library, London.

[8] Ministry of Health, Final Report of the Voluntary Hospitals Commission (Chairman, Lord Cave), Cmd 1335 HMSO, 1921.

[9] The Hospitals - 1800 to 1948, A Study in Social Administration in England & Wales, Heinemann, Brian Abel-Smith, 1964, Harvard University Press.

[10] The Hospitals of the United Kingdom, Bristowe, J.S. & Holmes T., Appendix 15 of Report to the Medical Officer of the Privy Council, HMSO 1863.

[11] Annual Report of the County Medical Officer of Health, Carmarthenshire, 31/12/1913, Carmarthenshire Archives Service.

35. Second World War – nursing staff, policeman and patient in the Infirmary garden, 1940.

36. Volunteers preparing dressings and bandages at the Infirmary during the Second World War, 1940.

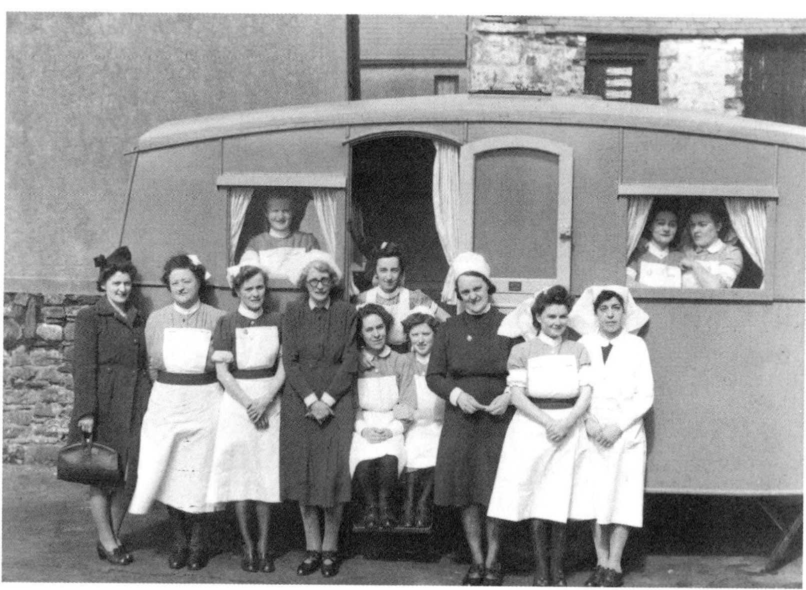

37. Nurses' caravan parked in the Infirmary forecourt, 1947.
Matron Dorothy Hartland, Sister Tutor Thomas and Della Evans 2nd from right – currently Chairman of the League of Friends of the West Wales General Hospital.

38. State Registered Nurse Finalists, 1948. Col. W.D. Williams centre front row, and Miss E. Miles, Matron from 1948 to 1955 to his left. Della Evans currently Chairman of the League of Friends 2nd row, first right.

39. 25th March, 1949 - first day on the Glangwili site.
Nursing and administrative staff with the County ambulance.

40. View of Glangwili Hospital taken facing the Dolgwili Road, 1949.

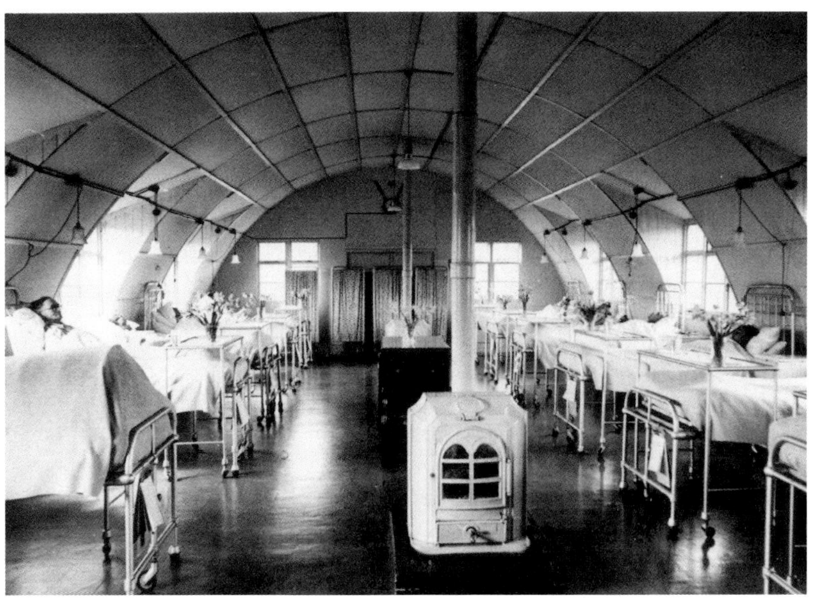

41. Female Medical Ward in a Nissen Hut, 1949

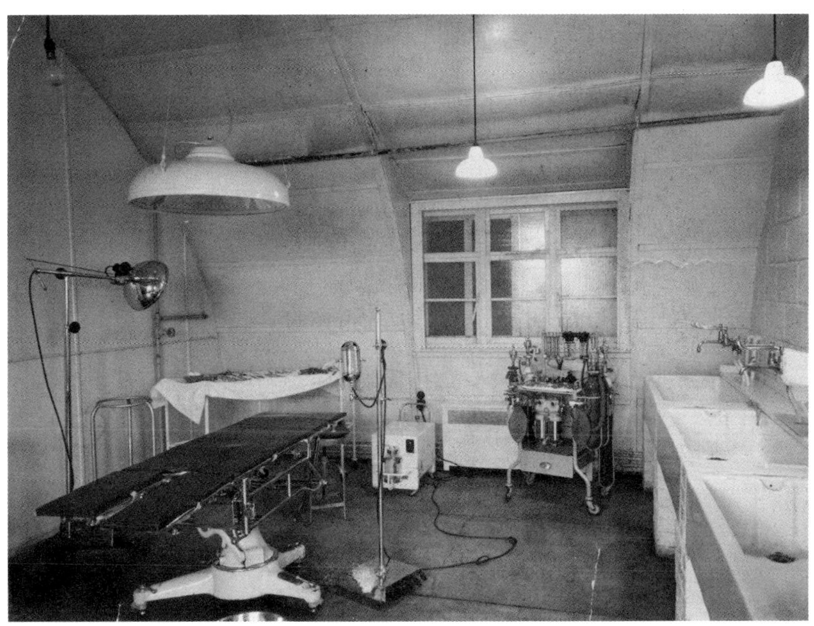

42. ENT Operating Theatre in a Nissen Hut, 1949

43. The hospital campus in 1949

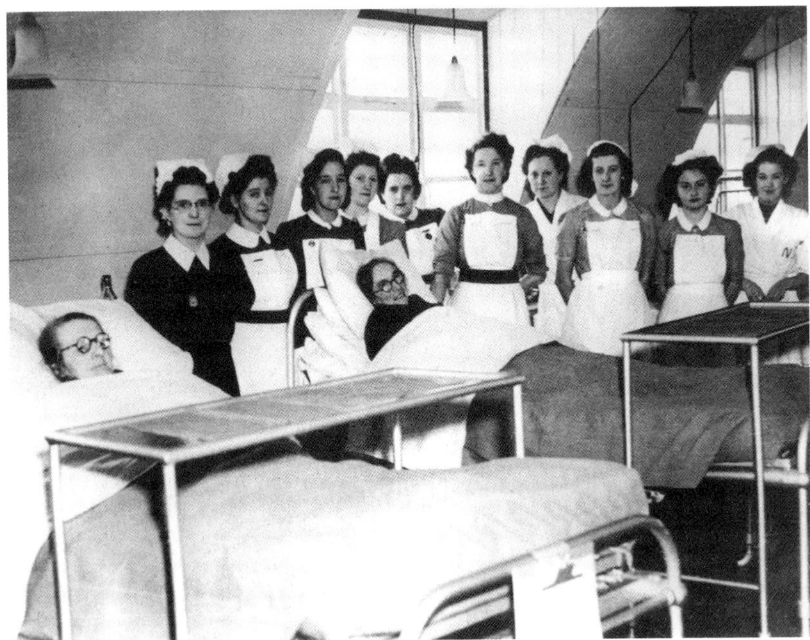

44. Nursing staff with the first 2 patients admitted to Glangwili Hospital on the 25th March, 1949

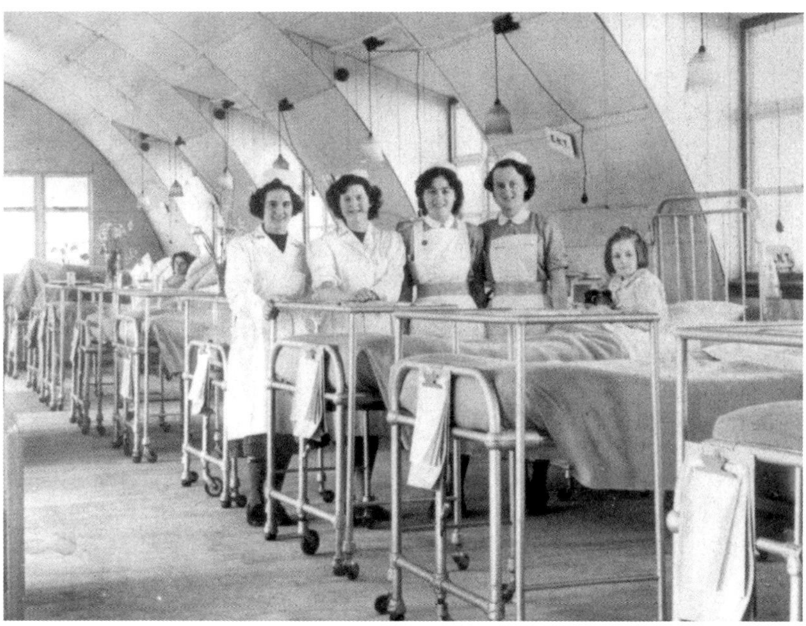

45. ENT section of ward with nursing staff, 1951

46. Bring and Buy Sale, 1956. Miss E.A. Lloyd, Assistant Matron first from right, Miss A. Sim, Matron from 1955 to 1958 sixth from right and Sister Dulcie Thomas, Theatre Superintendent, seventh from right

47. West Wales General Hospital School of Nursing - classroom in a Nissen Hut on the Glangwili site, 1965

48. West Wales General Hospital, 1956 - Ward Block 1, first Nurses Home and Recreation Centre (Cambrian Room) under construction.

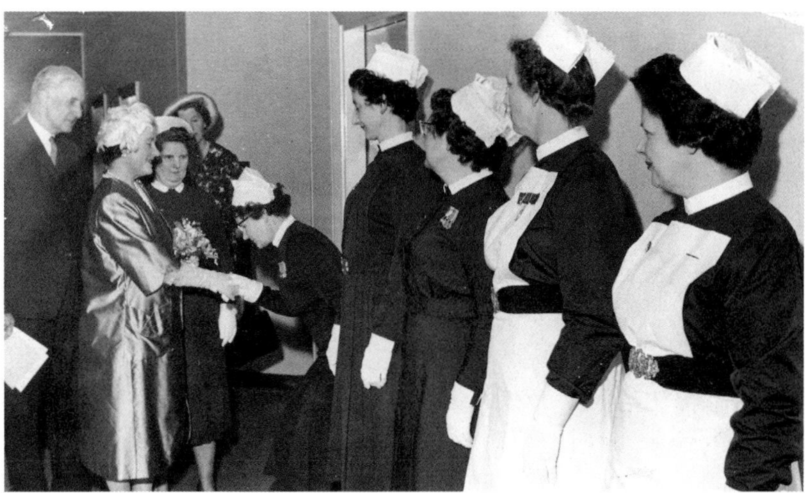

49. H.M. Queen Elizabeth, the Queen Mother with Matron John to her left meeting Miss E.A. Lloyd, Assistant Matron. Also in the picture from right to left, Sister P. Evans, Sister M.L. Goodfellow, Administrative Sister Miss I.M. Emmanuel and Miss E. Walters, Sister Tutor. Thursday, 28th May, 1959

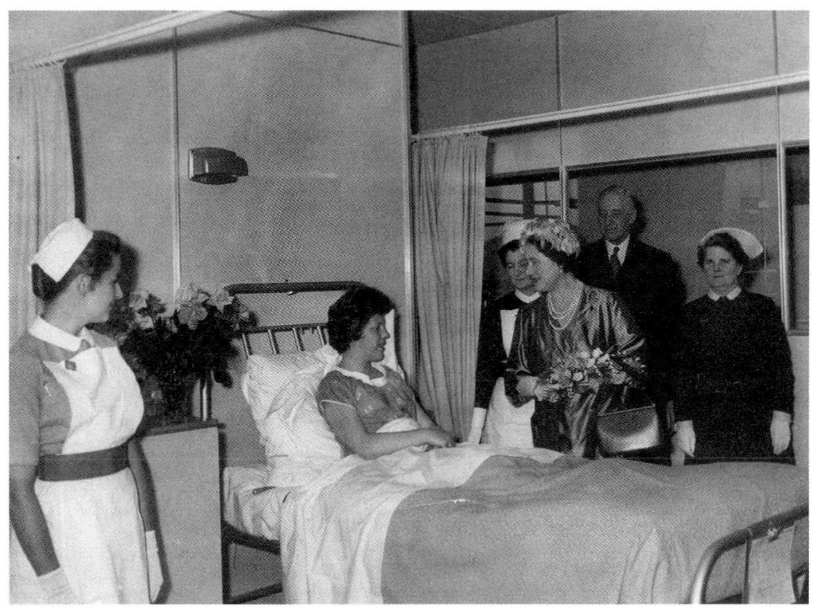

50. The Queen Mother meeting a patient on Towy Ward, Sister Sadie Morris to Her Majesty's left and Matron John to her right, 28th May, 1959

51. West Wales General Hospital, December, 1965.

52. Nurses' Homes 1 & 2, 1965.

53. West Wales General Hospital, December, 1967.

54. Christmas Concert, 1966.

55. Retirement party for Mr. D.C. Williams, Consultant General Surgeon from 1948 to 1972 at the Ivy Bush Royal Hotel.

56. Miss Linda Ditcham, R.R.C.,
Matron from 1898 to 1926.

57. Miss Dorothy Hartland,
Matron from 1926 to 1948.

58. Miss C.B.M. John,
Matron from 1958 to 1961.

59. Miss Arfona Vaughan-Jones,
Matron from 1961 to 1974.

60. County Infirmary, Carmarthen – Hospital Badge awarded on completion of training and passing the final examination for State Registered Nurses.

61. West Wales General Hospital, Carmarthen – Hospital Badge awarded on completion of training and passing the final examination for State Registered Nurses.

<u>CHAPTER VII</u>

THE NATIONAL HEALTH SERVICE AND THE WEST WALES GENERAL HOSPITAL

It has been seen that, from the middle of the nineteenth century, people had come to believe that access to health care was part of the structure of a civilized society.

In 1948 there was a chaotic mixture of large and small, public and private hospitals which had developed in a haphazard manner bearing little relation to proven need. The Second World War had served, like the First, to confirm that the existing system, both for the provision and for the financing of health services, was becoming unworkable. R.M. Titmuss pointed out that, in 1939:

> *"...of about 700 general voluntary hospitals only 75 had over 200 beds, some 115 had between 100 and 200 beds, over 500 had less than 100 beds and more than half of those had less than 30 beds."*[1]

It was believed that, in these small hospitals, the really bad medical care was provided. Specialist services were distributed according to the economics of private practice, not of need. Hospital planning, therefore, was seen to be crucial. Unfortunately, after the First World War, no agreement could be reached on what needed to be done although the Labour Party before the War and the left wing Fabian Society during it had advocated the establishment of an authoritarian and paternalistic National Health Service. Then, in 1920, the Royal Commission chaired by Lord Dawson of Penn in their *"Report on the Future Provision of Medical and Allied Services"*[2] followed, in 1921, by Lord Cave's Commission in their *"Report on Voluntary Hospitals and their Services"*[3] came to opposite conclusions. Lord Dawson of Penn, formerly Sir Bertrand Dawson, Consultant Physician to The London Hospital, President of the Royal College of Physicians and the most influential doctor of his day, favoured a complete remodelling of the nation's health services with central planning, financing and control – a National Health Service. Lord Cave's Commission concluded that although an immediate grant was needed to avert financial disaster the Voluntary Hospitals should remain independent of state control and bureaucratic meddling (see page 161-2).

Despite the continuing efforts of Lord Dawson, no action was taken until after the Second World War when experience of the central direction of a huge and successful war effort by Winston Churchill's Coalition Government, as well as the efficiency of the Emergency Medical Service, had done much to dispel fears of bureaucratic interference.[11] The war also produced, for the first time, a strong sense of social solidarity. Most doctors had had military experience and knew that service personnel had received better healthcare than civilians and were broadly in favour of change.[11]

The Beveridge Report on 'Social Insurance and Allied Services' was published in 1942 and based its recommendations on the assumption that a "free" National Health Service would be established.[4] In 1943, the Ministry of Health, considered transforming the Emergency Medical Service, after the war, into a comprehensive health service, free and available to all.[5] On these foundations, the White Paper, 'A National Health Service' was published in early 1944, advocating its introduction.[6] It was accepted by the Conservative Cabinet in the interval between the wartime coalition government and the election of Clement Attlee's Labour government in August, 1945 and the appointment of the Welsh miners' leader, Aneurin (Nye) Bevan, as Minister of Health. He established a nationalised service under the direct control of the Minister. New District Management Committees and Regional Health Boards were appointed, not elected. Bevan himself soon came to regret this *"defect"*, saying that *"election is a better principle than selection."*[7]

The support of the doctors, then a powerful profession, subsequently emasculated by left wing Governments, was crucial to the whole enterprise. The ground had been prepared by the British Medical Association that had published its recommendations of support in, 'A General Medical Service for the Nation' in 1938[8] adumbrated by a similar report published in 1929.[9] This support was endorsed by the Lancet's "Commissioner", Dr Stephen Taylor, in 'A Plan for British Hospitals' published on the 28th October, 1939.[10] The acquiescence of the consultants was, finally, secured by conceding, as Richard Crossman, the Labour Minister in Harold Wilson's 1964 to 1970 Government, pointed out:

> *"…an entrenched position that could not be broken without jeopardizing the whole health service."*[11]

These concessions were summed up by Professor Abel-Smith as follows:

> *"…not only were they to be paid for what they had previously done for nothing, they were also to have private patients and treat them on the spot. As Bevan remarked to a friend, 'I stuffed their mouths with gold'…..thus the top doctors had obtained 'a la suite terms' in the Health Service: heavy representation on Regional and District Boards, control of hospital beds, loosely defined sessions, the secret disposal of Treasury funds to those of their number the Presidents of the Medical Royal Colleges thought more meritorious, the lions share of teaching hospital endowments for their research and the right to private practice."*[7]

Moreover, no provision to monitor the quality of care, as already existed in the United States, had been made. At the Carmarthen Infirmary, however, the very first instance of quality assurance monitoring was a study of Outpatient waiting times in 1947 which was followed by recommendations for improvement! 60 years later, the weekly Grand Rounds and monthly Morbidity/Mortality Meetings considered by American physicians to be the most valuable of all Quality Assurance activities are not a regular feature of NHS hospital practice.

Fortunately, the National Health Service was seen by the public, and most of the non-consultant doctors, as a measure to improve the quality and quantity of medical services and was, and is, widely supported. GPs were given a special place, with elaborate safeguards, which kept them isolated from the hospitals and from the community services, which were left in the hands of the local authorities and their medical officers of health.

The Service was to be based on the ideal of universal coverage for all British citizens, paid for from general tax revenues. Its founding principles were those of: *"equity"* - all British residents should have equal access to health care, *"comprehensiveness"* - all aspects of preventive and curative medicine should be provided and that there should be *"no charge at the point of service"* to separate access to healthcare from the ability to pay.[12]

Hospital services, family practitioner services (doctors, pharmacists, opticians and dentists) and community-based services were brought into one organization for the first time. The service was divided into three parts:

1. Hospital services.

2. Family doctors, dentists, opticians and pharmacists who remained self-employed under a contract from an Executive Council.

3. Local authority health services including community nursing, midwifery, health visiting, maternal and infant welfare clinics, immunisation and the control of infectious diseases.

It had been hard to anticipate the day-to-day costs of the new service and public expectations had risen. Medical science was rapidly gathering pace, new treatments and drugs were being developed and hospitals for tuberculosis and infectious diseases were being closed to release funds for new services.[11] Home delivery supported by the "obstetric flying-squad" was giving way to hospital delivery for most mothers, rheumatic heart disease was being treated surgically, and the first hip replacements were being performed.[11] Within three years of its creation, rapidly rising costs forced the NHS to introduce some modest fees.[11] Prescription charges of one shilling (5p), which had been legislated for as early as 1949 but not implemented, were introduced in 1952. A flat rate of £1 for ordinary dental treatment was brought in at the same time.[11]

The scope of the NHS has narrowed since its inception - dental care, eye care and prescription charges, for example, are not covered and there always has been a private system that operates parallel to the public system. While everyone is covered by the NHS, people are permitted to buy insurance or any medical service from private insurers and health providers, respectively. About 12% of the U.K. population has private medical insurance, although one fifth of private patients do not have insurance and pay directly when they need treatment.[12]

The Ministry of Health Hospital Survey, issued in 1945, concurred with the estimate made in 1930; that a hospital of 450 beds was the ultimate aim for the Carmarthen district.[13] One of the surveyors for South Wales was Dr. Alan Trevor Jones, formerly a member of the Infirmary medical staff, and this publication, no doubt, provided the impetus for initiating the correspondence, with the War Office, with regard to the acquisition of the former American Military Hospital site at Glangwili which commenced in early 1946 because it was feared that the new hospital that was, clearly, required might be built in Llanelly or Haverfordwest. Dr. Healy confirmed that, even before the outbreak of war, the medical staff fully realised that more beds were needed and that further expansion on the Infirmary site was not possible. Discussions began with regard to demolishing the Old Infirmary and erecting a modern building elsewhere. One of the sites under consideration was Friars Park. In fact, proposals were being made to take over part of the American Military Hospital well before it became clear that the Government was going take over the voluntary hospitals. The Medical Staff also became interested in setting-up facilities for the provision of *"deep X-ray therapy"* at this time.

In December, 1946, Sir Rhys Hopkin Morris, K.C. M.P. for Carmarthen arranged for a deputation to be received by the Secretary of State for War in the new Attlee government, The Rt. Hon. F.W. Bellinger, M.P. The deputation consisting of the President, Col. W. D. Williams, the Chairman, The Rev. Waldo B. Lewis, Dr. J. J. Healy, Dr. C. F. Parry, and Mr. J. R. E. James evidently impressed the Minister by their appeal for in February, 1947 the Committee was notified that 100 beds in the War Department Hospital had been allocated to the Infirmary.[14]

The United States Army Corps of Engineers had built a hospital camp on both sides of the Dolgwili Road in 1942 on land requisitioned by the War Office. It was intended for battle casualties from the "Second Front" (following the D-Day Normandy invasion of France on the 6th June, 1944) and contained 750 beds but was little used. Facing in the direction of Carmarthen town, the main hospital camp was on the left, the site of the present hospital and the permanent staff lived in a smaller camp on the right hand side of the road behind the houses. The hospital camp consisted entirely of Nissen huts which had been developed by Peter Norman Nissen, a Canadian mining engineer, for the British War Office in 1916. They consisted of sheets of corrugated steel bent into half a cylinder and planted in the ground with the axis horizontal. The semicircular ends were enclosed with masonry walls. The staff camp was comprised of large tents and a few Nissen huts.

The American Military left the area in July, 1945 after the German unconditional surrender on the 8th May and the hospital was surrounded with barbed wire and used by the War Office from the 14th July, as a prisoner-of-war hospital for sick and wounded Germans. The Commandant was a Colonel in the Royal Army Medical Corps supported by a Chief Administrative Medical Officer, also R.A.M.C., and an Adjutant, Captain K. J. Gale, Royal Artillery. The camp was guarded by the Royal Military Police, the contingent consisting of 3 officers and only 17 other ranks! The Chief Interrogator was an Austrian Jew. The hospital was permanently staffed by 222 German prisoners from the Wehrmacht Medical Department of whom 30 were doctors and well over 100 were "Krankenwaerter" (male nurses) to care for often up to 900 patients. In 1946, 2 patients from the camp were transferred to Nuremberg to appear before the War Crimes Tribunal and were, subsequently, sentenced to death.[15]

Occasionally, one of the senior German Physicians would be escorted to 'Island Farm Special Camp 11' near Bridgend to examine and treat senior German officers being held there. These included the Field Marshals Gerd von Rundstedt, Erich von Manstein and Ewald von Kleist. The last German patients left in November, 1947 and the camp was abandoned by the Army in December, 1947.[15]

The problems of administering a modern hospital had become increasingly more complex and the burdens of the two part-time Honorary Secretaries, J. Arthur Jones and John Saer, at the Infirmary, more onerous. In 1938 an experienced full-time Secretary was appointed, Mr. G. Bertram Isaac. When Mr. Isaac retired in September 1947 he was replaced as "Chief Administrative Officer" by Mr. A. W. Youngs, F.C.I.S., F.H.A who, to quote the report of 1947, had had 18 years experience of hospital administration including 7 years in senior appointments.[14] In 1952 he was succeeded by Mr. N.A. Ball, F.H.A who served for nearly 18 years.

Fourteen Regional Hospital Boards had been set up by the Act from which the teaching hospitals were excluded and the Boards then allotted hospitals to groups and set up 377 Hospital Management Committees. On the "appointed" day Mr. Youngs became the Group Secretary and Supplies Officer of the newly-formed West Wales Hospital Management Committee, based at the Carmarthenshire Infirmary, assisted by a Finance Officer, Mr. T. W. Joshua, A.S.A.A., formerly Secretary-Superintendent of Llanelly General Hospital.[16]

The Chairman of the Infirmary Management Committee, The Rev. Waldo B. Lewis (died 1953), became a member of the Regional Health Authority and Chairman of the NHS West Wales Hospital Management Committee on the "appointed day". Thus we find Carmarthen in the happy position of providing both the new Chairman and the Group Secretary under the National Health Service. A full interpretation is not possible, not only because of the reluctance of the principals to discuss the matter with us but, also, because of the mysterious disappearance of the Minute Books which cover the period 1942 to 1948. Certainly, geographical factors and the foresight of the Committee in acquiring the wartime American Military Hospital and site, at Glangwili, from the War Office which meant the availability of accommodation for Group Offices and, also, fine building land for a new hospital overlooking the River Towy, perhaps, explains why Carmarthen was selected as the area base for hospital development. The manoeuvres of the Management Committee and the Medical Staff of the Infirmary during the last 10 years of its existence, as an independent entity, appear to have been very far-sighted.

In the West Wales area, in 1947, there was, as described, a whole range of different types of hospitals, large and small, run by voluntary committees or local authorities covering various specialties. With the introduction of the National Health Service the hospitals that managed all non-psychiatric cases in Pembrokeshire, West Carmarthenshire and South Cardiganshire were grouped together as one administrative unit under the management of the newly formed West Wales Hospital Management Committee. Routine meetings were held on a rotating basis at all the institutions for which the Committee were responsible. In July, 1951, it is recorded that they very much a enjoyed a meeting on board the Fishguard–Rosslare steamer, the S.S. St. David, in Fishguard Harbour. The Mental Hospitals in the area were also grouped to form the Carmarthen Mental Hospital Management Committee. These two Management Committees were responsible for the provision of hospital services in the West Wales area to the Welsh Regional Hospital Board (later this latter authority dropped the word "Regional" from its title by Act of Parliament). The Welsh Regional Hospital Board was in turn responsible to the Welsh Board of Health, the Ministry of Health's Welsh Office.

The 13 hospitals[16] to be administered by the new West Wales Hospital Management Committee were:

Acute General Hospitals	Beds
West Wales General Hospital, Carmarthen	102
Pembroke County War Memorial Hospital, Haverfordwest (now Withy Bush)	120

Cardigan and District Hospital, Cardigan	10
Tenby Cottage Hospital, Tenby	10
Meyrick Hospital, Pembroke Dock	16
Pembroke Cottage Hospital, Pembroke	10
Llandovery Cottage Hospital, Llandovery	10

<u>Tuberculosis Hospitals</u>

Kensington Hospital, St. Brides, Haverfordwest	100
Sealyham Hospital, Wolf's Castle, Pembrokeshire	35
West Wales Sanatorium, Llanybyther (became a Chest Hospital until 1968 then Allt-y-Mynydd Hospital – closed in 1986)	47

<u>Infectious Diseases Hospitals</u>

Pembroke County Isolation Hospital, Pembroke Dock (designated a General Hospital in 1949),	24
Sandy Haven Isolation Hospital, Milford Haven (closed in 1949).	0
West Wales Isolation Hospital, Upper Tumble, Llanelly (now Mynydd Mawr Hospital)	62

The Penlan Hospital, in the old workhouse, with 38 beds for the elderly and chronic sick was managed jointly with the County Council until it closed in 1972 on the reopening of Priory Street Hospital.

The ex-Military Hospital, with all its equipment (an unexpected bonus), was formally handed over by the War Office to the Infirmary in October, 1947 and, with 32 beds staffed, was re-opened by the West Wales Hospital Management Committee on the 25th March, 1949 and named the West Wales General Hospital.[16] The site was shared, initially, with the Post Office Telephone Department, the Ministry of Works and the Carmarthenshire Agricultural Society. Shortly thereafter two further huts of 32 beds each were staffed and opened along with a General and an ENT Operating Theatre. At this time the Infirmary was renamed Priory Street Hospital and a 12hp Morris shooting brake (estate car) was purchased to shuttle staff and equipment between the two sites and soon became known as "the brake". These trips were often made at very short notice as instruments and equipment were shared between the two hospitals.

The correspondence with the War Office was handed over to Major Francis Jones, County Archivist, by Mr. J. R. E. James on the 18th September, 1965 at a ceremony attended by the Secretary of State for Wales, The Rt. Hon. James Griffiths, M.P. but was not entered in the Accession Register and cannot be found in the Archives at the time of writing.[16]

The vision of the Hospital Management Committee is clearly illustrated in its first Report published in 1949:

> *"In the meantime plans will be prepared for a new hospital of 300 beds on this excellent site to provide a really first class hospital centre for the area."*[16]

On the 6th January 1953 the Conservative Minister of Health, Mr. Iain MacLeod, visited the ex-military hospital site or "Glangwili", as it soon became known, with senior Ministry and Welsh Hospital Board officials. The Hospital Management Committee took this golden opportunity to press their claim for the erection of a permanent hospital on the site. The Minister was shown the worst of the hutted accommodation which had been occupied and it was, respectfully, suggested that money was being poured down the drain in an endeavour to improve conditions.

The Minister gave a verbal promise that he would see if something could be done. Here, apparently, was one politician who was as good as his word. In February, 1955 he announced the very first programme of hospital building since the National Health Service came into being.[17] The development of the West Wales General Hospital on the Glangwili site was included at an approximate cost of £1.5 million. The hospital was to be built in stages. As it turned out the cost estimate was to prove a little too optimistic the final total being nearer £2.5 million. The building of the new hospital in stages, for financial reasons, meant that the new buildings only very slowly digested the sprawling network of huts.

Complications arose due to the development by stages. Long temporary communicating corridors and the uncertainty of the continuity of one building contractor, are some examples. Fortunately, Messrs. E. Turner & Sons of Cardiff were successful in tendering for all of the 4 stages of the hospital to the design of Sir Percy Thomas and Sons also of Cardiff.

Stage I January, 1956 to March, 1958

> The foundation stone was laid by Miss Patricia Hornsby-Smith, M.P. Parliamentary Secretary to the Ministry of Health in October, 1956. This stage consisted of the Boiler House, the first section of the Nurses' Home and a ward block of 96 beds. The work was completed in March, 1958 at a cost of £164,887 and the buildings were officially opened by Her Majesty, Queen Elizabeth, the Queen Mother on the 28th May 1959. The Queen Mother, in her address, stressed that development on the site would be for the benefit of the whole area:
>
> " *For twenty years men and women of vision have dreamed of a better hospital service for this county and since this site was made available, they have set a fine example of far-sighted imagination; first in putting to good use the discouragingly derelict huts, and then in seizing the opportunity to develop a hospital – not for this locality only but for the whole of West Wales."*[1]

Stage 2 May, 1959 to February, 1961

> With the second stage came a further Ward Block of 96 beds; the Stores and Catering Departments; the Outpatients and Casualty Departments together with the Pathological and Public Health Laboratories costing £382,582.

It is interesting to note that in January 1962 the Ministry of Health published yet another document which was to consolidate the position of hospital services in Carmarthen. In *"A Hospital Plan for England &*

Wales" an outline of proposals was given in an attempt to further rationalize the pattern of hospital provision under the Health Service. It introduced the concept of *"Base District General Hospitals"* and recognized the need to bring together under one roof a wide range of diagnostic and treatment facilities even if this meant the closure of small, scattered local hospitals. This then confirmed the original intention of local enthusiasts some 15 years previously that Carmarthen should become the main hospital centre for the population of 180,000 covered by the Hospital Management Committee. The Ministry's document stated that:

> *"The district general hospital offers the most practicable method of placing of placing the full range of hospital facilities at the disposal of patients and this consideration far outweighs the disadvantages of longer travel for some patients and visitors."*[18]

Stage 3 July, 1962 to November, 1964

> This stage extended the accommodation available for resident staff at a cost of £145,878. An extension was added to the Nurses Home providing an additional 70 rooms. In addition 4 houses were provided for Matron and senior members of the medical staff.

On 1st April 1963 the West Wales Hospital Management Committee and the Carmarthen Mental Hospital Management Committee were merged to form the South West Wales Hospital Management Committee. This brought together, in one administrative unit, both general and psychiatric hospital facilities including St. David's Hospital with its 1,000 beds. This was in line with national policy and this unity is emphasized by the provision of psychiatric facilities in the final stage of the building programme, [19]

Stage 4 December, 1964 to December, 1968

> The 4th and last stage of development, costing £1,729,000, consisted of:

1. Ward Block 3 of 96 beds

2. Ward Block 4 of 108 beds incorporating beds for psychiatric patients and a Psychiatric Day Centre.

3. Further accommodation for single and married junior medical staff.

4. An Administrative block housing both Group and hospital administrative staff together with post mortem, pathology and pharmacy departments.

5. A curved building linking all the ward blocks which provided accommodation for the following departments: Nurse Training School, CSSD, Library, Chapel, Physiotherapy, X-ray, Operating Theatres, Central Linen Room, Maternity Delivery Suite and Special Care Baby Unit and overnight accommodation for the relatives of seriously ill patients.

6. A Laundry serving all the hospitals in the area which became operational in January 1966. The laundry was claimed to be one of the most modern in Europe with a high degree of mechanization and incorporating barriers between the clean and dirty areas.

7. Engineering and Garage Workshops which were brought into use during the summer of 1966.

The new hospital was fully operational by December, 1968. It was the first completely new district general hospital in Wales to be built under the auspices of the National Health Service and provided a comprehensive hospital service to most of West Wales. Great care was taken to ensure that the buildings fitted into the landscape and the emphasis was on grass and trees. The whole picture was in tremendous contrast to the humble beginnings of hospital provision in Carmarthen.

The old Infirmary continued as an acute facility but as the new wards and departments opened on the Glangwili site, it gradually reduced its activities until only Obstetrics & Gynaecology (Mr. J.R.E. James) and some General Surgery (Mr. D.C. Williams) remained. All acute services were finally transferred to Glangwili in 1969 when the construction of car parks and landscaping had been completed. The Infirmary was then remodelled so that eventually it provided 67 geriatric beds plus 8 orthopaedic rehabilitation beds and a 12 place Day Hospital. A new boiler house with automatic oil-fired boilers was built. The admission of long stay geriatric patients began in 1972 and the old Penlan geriatric ward was finally closed.

By 1968 the total number of beds at the West Wales General Hospital (including Priory Street Hospital) was 502. In 1971, 12,213 inpatients, 37,645 outpatients and 13,280 Accident & Emergency patients were treated at a cost of £1,389,425. At this time the Management Committee requested the Welsh Hospital Board to provide funds for a Day Surgery Centre, an Intensive Care Unit, a Postgraduate Medical Centre, a unit for the young chronic sick and an extension to the Pathology Department. Unfortunately, it was more than a decade before funds were made available.

On the 1st April, 1974 the National Health Service Reorganisation Act became operational. Its aim was to provide an integrated health service incorporating hospital services, family practitioner services and all the health functions of local authorities. Thus the new Dyfed Area Health Authority was formed from the Hospital Management Committees of South West Wales, Mid-Wales and Glantawe, the Health Departments of Carmarthenshire, Cardiganshire and Pembrokeshire and the Executive Councils of those counties. Its boundaries coincided with those of the new local government area. The Authority was subdivided into four Health Districts; Carmarthen/Dinefwr, Ceredigion, Llanelli/Dinefwr and Preseli/South Pembrokeshire District. The Carmarthen/Dinefwr Health District took over responsibility for the West Wales General Hospital and Priory Street Hospital with a total of

518 beds, St. David's Hospital with 813 beds and Llandovery Cottage Hospital with 18 beds The old TB/Chest Hospital, Llanybyther renamed Allt-y-Mynydd Hospital re-opened in 1970 with 60 beds for mentally handicapped patients after the provision, in 1967, of services for "Chest" patients at Glangwili. By 1974 an Assessment Unit, a 32 bed unit for mentally handicapped children and a 14 bed unit for the elderly mentally infirm had been opened. The Psychiatric Day Unit at Glangwili then became a Day Centre for all patient groups.[20]

Following reorganisation the NHS was still in crisis when the Royal Commission on the NHS reported in July, 1979. The report suggested that there were too many management tiers, too many administrators, a failure to take quick decisions and a waste of money. The remedies suggested were strengthening local management, simplification by removing the area tier, simplification of professional advisory machinery and simplification of the planning system. 192 District Health Authorities replaced 90 Area Health Authorities. On the 1st April, 1982, the East Dyfed District Health Authority became responsible for the healthcare needs of 235,000 people in an area of 1,615 square miles. It was subdivided into 4 health management units; Aberystwyth, Carmarthen/Dinefwr, Llanelli/Dinefwr and the Mental Health Unit. The Pembrokeshire District Health Authority took over all responsibilities in that county.[21]

In 1988 the Carmarthen/Dinefwr Health Management Unit had a revenue budget of £19.6 million, 1,277 employees and 463 beds at the West Wales General Hospital, Priory Street Hospital and Llandovery Cottage Hospital. Allt-y-Mynydd Hospital had closed in 1986 and some beds in Priory Street had been closed as community services were developed. 14,600 inpatients and 82,000 outpatients were treated at the West Wales General Hospital in 1988 compared with 2,461 inpatients and 7,382 outpatients at a cost of £56,000 treated at the Infirmary in 1948.[22]

In 1948 there were 47 deaths from TB and 16 new cases of polio in Carmarthen; in 1988 there were none. Deaths from kidney disease were 31 in 1948 but in 1987 only 6 patients succumbed. Infant mortality was reduced from 40 to only 6 although deaths from cancer, strokes and road traffic accidents increased during the 40 year period. In 1948 the population was growing but by 1987 the death-rate exceeded the birth-rate so that healthcare providers were faced with a decreasing and ageing population.[22]

A 6 bedded Intensive Care Unit was opened at the West Wales General Hospital in 1985 along with a satellite (of Morriston Hospital) Renal Dialysis Unit which, initially, dialysed 9 patients 27 times per week. The Postgraduate Medical Centre was opened in 1986, a new Special Care Baby Unit in May, 1988 and a 6 bedded Coronary Care Unit in November, 1989. A purpose-built acute psychiatric inpatient ward and Day Hospital had been completed in 1986 when structural defects were discovered in the four main Ward Blocks at Glangwili requiring major reconstruction which continued until April, 1995 and prevented the planned closure of Priory Street Hospital. The opportunity was taken to modernise and refurbish all the ward blocks at a total cost of £8.1 million.[23]

The 1990 NHS and Community Care Act changed both the philosophy and, once again, the organisation of healthcare. A Cabinet Committee chaired by the Prime Minister, Margaret Thatcher, had decided to improve productivity by reforming incentives and management and introducing market forces into the NHS. Neither the medical profession nor, indeed, any other group of healthcare professionals were consulted. Health authorities would concentrate on the assessment of need and would contract for services with hospitals and community units thus separating the functions of purchase and service.[11] Hospitals would be allowed to become "self-governing" as Trusts and would be able to employ staff, negotiate terms and conditions of service, own and dispose of their assets, retain surpluses and borrow money from the government and the private sector.[11] They would generate revenue by making contracts with health districts, commissioning agencies and G.P. fundholders.[11] Dr. Rivett points out that this was a model well-suited to elective surgery but less appropriate for the elderly and for psychiatric services.

> *"Markets have winner and losers; would the poor, deprived and handicapped be at risk?"*

The Carmarthen and District NHS Trust was established on the 1st April, 1993 and was responsible for providing a full range of hospital and community healthcare services to the population of 90,000 in Carmarthen and the surrounding areas. A range of sub-specialties was made available for the total population of Dyfed of 236,000. The West Wales General Hospital, Priory Street Hospital and Llandovery Cottage Hospital became the responsibility of the Trust. In 1993/1994 1,430 staff treated 27,300 inpatients (including Day Cases), 83,900 outpatients and 24,380 Accident & Emergency cases at a cost of £37 million. 44% of all elective treatment was undertaken on a day care basis. A Day Surgical Unit and Endoscopy Suite was opened in October, 1995 and increased this percentage to 70%. The Intensive Care Unit was remodelled in 1995 to provide 3 intensive care and 3 high dependency beds.[23]

In 1995 the East Dyfed Health Authority was replaced by the Dyfed Powys Health Authority which, itself, was dissolved in 2003 to be replaced by Local Health Boards (LHBs) coterminous with local authority boundaries. LHBs plan local healthcare policy, assess need and pay family doctors, dentists, opticians, pharmacists and other professionals for primary care, hospital trusts for secondary, tertiary and community care in partnership with local social services. Most services are now provided by NHS Trusts including primary care. In Wales there are now 22 Local Health Boards and 14 NHS Trusts. In 2004/2005 the NHS Wales will spend £4.2 billion and employ 81,000 staff – 7% of the working population of Wales and its largest employer. A single organisation covering the whole of Wales, the National Public Health Service gives advice and guidance to Local Health Boards on a range of issues such as disease control and prevention as well as child protection. The Carmarthenshire Local Health Board is based in Llanelli. There are Community Health Councils in each of the 22 local government areas in Wales and they take up a wide range of health issues on behalf of the public.[24]

The Priory Day Hospital on the Glangwili site was planned by the hospital's own medical, nursing, paramedical, technical and management staff. It was designed and the contract project managed by the Trust's architects and engineering staff. It is situated adjacent to the rehabilitation wards and cost a total of £1.4 million On the 15th January, 1996 it was, appropriately, opened by Mr. D.T.P. Rogers, M.B.E., J.P. Mr. Rogers had served as a member of the South West Wales Hospital Management Committee. Subsequently, he became Secretary of the League of Friends of the West Wales General Hospital and, for many years, Chairman until he retired in 2004 at the age of 86 after 40 years service to the hospitals.[23]

On Sunday, the 25th February, 1996 patients from Llwyd and Hawen Wards at Priory Street Hospital were transferred to the new Dyfrig and Cadog wards at the West Wales General Hospital. The end of an era was signalled on the 31st March, 1996 when Priory Street Hospital was formally closed after almost a century and a half of service to the people of Carmarthenshire. It was put on the market for £250,000 and sold to a developer in October, 1998 for £50,000 for conversion into apartments. As a Grade II Listed Building, the façade, with the proud inscription, "CARMARTHENSHIRE INFIRMARY - SUPPORTED BY VOLUNTARY CONTRIBUTIONS - FOUNDED 1847 - BUILT 1858", will be preserved. It was reported that there was a loss to the National Health Service of £120,000, at the time of sale, because security and other costs had amounted to some £170,000.[25]

The new Labour Government published a White Paper in 1998 confirming its intention to reform the National Health Service. It proposed to replace the competition of the internal market with improved cooperation and collaboration within the NHS and with local government and the voluntary sector and to reduce the number of Trusts. On the 1st April, 1999, after formal public consultation over the summer of 1998, the Welsh Assembly Government merged the Carmarthen and District NHS Trust with the Llanelli/Dinefwr NHS Trust. Both had been found to be small, inefficient Trusts with duplicated services. The Carmarthenshire NHS Trust now provides acute and community healthcare services to the population of 170,000 in Carmarthenshire and parts of neighbouring counties.[24]

Acute and emergency services are provided at the West Wales General Hospital with 383 beds and the Prince Philip Hospital, Llanelli with 238 beds. There are support, continuing care and rehabilitation inpatient beds at Amman Valley, Llandovery and Mynydd Mawr Hospitals with a total of 64 beds. Bryntirion Hospital closed in 2003 and its services were transferred to Prince Philip Hospital. Mental Health Services are provided by the Pembrokeshire and Derwen NHS Trust and ambulance services by the Welsh Ambulance Services Trust.[24]

The Commission for Health Improvement (CHI) was set up in September, 1999 to support the development of high quality clinical practice consistently across the NHS. It carried out an investigation of the Trust in 2000 following some high-profile incidents which attracted close media scrutiny including the removal of a wrong kidney at Prince Philip Hospital and the subsequent death of the patient. The Report commented that the merger was unpopular and that the incidents served to undermine confidence in the new Trust. The 40 year old hospital buildings at Glangwili were thought to be cramped and not ideal for modern clinical practice. Senior administrative staff structure and clinical governance arrangements were also criticised.[26] A follow-up review of the Trust in 2003 was mostly favourable and produced further recommendations which are being implemented successfully. The functions of the CHI were taken over by the Healthcare Commission on the 1st April, 2004

Since the 1st April, 1999 the Trust has had the statutory duty of Clinical Governance placed upon it with ultimate responsibility resting with the Chief Executive.[24] It is a comprehensive Quality Assurance Programme and had been set up nearly 80 years after the United States introduced the concept. Apart from terminology, it is based on the American system. The key objective of Quality Assurance is to monitor patient outcomes which are influenced by the facility, its equipment and every category of staff. Immediate remedial action is taken when failings are identified so that the highest international standards are ensured. The grandiloquently named advisory body the "National Institute for Clinical Excellence" (NICE) set up by the government in April, 1999 could, perhaps more appropriately, be called the National Institute for Evidence-Based Medicine. NICE guidelines should be evidence-based but seem, too often, to be concerned with costs rather than benefits.

The King's Fund was founded in 1897 to raise money for London's voluntary hospitals. After the NHS was set-up in 1948 it broadened its activities and has offered nationwide hospital accreditation based on strictly defined standards of quality since the 1980s. The West Wales General Hospital satisfied these criteria in 1994 and again in 1997. However, there is still no comparable body in the United Kingdom to the American "Joint Commission for the Accreditation of Healthcare Organizations" (JCAHO). Its original foundation was initiated in 1920 by the American College of Surgeons, itself, founded in 1913. In 1953 it became an independent body which published standards that mandated quality assurance activities and supervised implementation. These standards were originally based on the "end result of hospital standardization" system proposed by Dr. Ernest Codman, a surgeon, in 1910. Under this system, a hospital would track every patient it treated long enough to determine whether the treatment was effective. If the treatment was not effective, the hospital would then attempt to determine why, so that similar cases could be treated successfully in the future. In 1970 standards were recast to represent optimal achievable levels of quality rather than minimum essential levels. Any hospital that cannot obtain accreditation for whatever reason does not survive. Its international division now inspects and accredits hospitals all over the world but not, as yet, in the United Kingdom!

The father of modern healthcare quality assurance is, undoubtedly, Dr. Avedis Donabedian of the University of Michigan. His seminal work, published in 1966, "Evaluating the Quality of Medical Care" which introduced the concepts of structure, process and outcome remains the dominant paradigm for the evaluation of quality healthcare to this day. This paper led to his 3 volumes on "Explorations in Quality Assessment and Monitoring" published in 1985.[27]

In the United States quality assurance activities were catalysed by the need for protection against the high risk of malpractice litigation where it is estimated that about 44,000 Americans are killed and hundreds of thousands injured every year by medical errors. This led, in the 1970s, to Multi-Disciplinary Team management of patients with major conditions such as the various cancers. The result was a significant improvement in outcomes and has now been adopted by the

NHS along with the production of clinical guidelines to gold standards of treatment. Most American hospitals employ Quality Assurance Consultants and Technicians who are responsible for data collection, ensuring timely and appropriate review and the implementation of remedial action. These activities, renamed "Clinical Governance", are now being introduced into the United Kingdom where it is known that there is about £4 billion outstanding in unresolved malpractice claims against the NHS. Chiefs of Service in the United States have now been joined by Clinical Directors in the United Kingdom and the previously unchallenged clinical freedom of consultants has been significantly eroded.

As early as 1966 Sir George Godber, Chief Medical Officer at the Ministry of Health, had set up a working party consisting mainly of Consultants to consider the organisation of medical work in hospitals. It reported the following year and became known as Cogwheel from the motif on its cover.[11] The importance of reviewing clinical work and its outcome was emphasised.[29] Apart from the setting up of clinical divisions no action was taken. Indeed, it is believed that the whole process of clinical review has been retarded in the United Kingdom by entrenched individualism and the culture of "Consultant is King". There is still a reluctance to focus on individual performance. The pendulum has now swung away from a Consultant-led service with the introduction of industrial management methods and jargon such as vision statements, missions and strategic plans. These are seen by some as inappropriate and unworkable in the healthcare setting and by others as a definite improvement.

The Chairman and the 7 Non-Executive Directors of the Carmarthenshire NHS Trust are salaried appointments made by the Welsh Assembly Government usually for a four year period. The Executive Directors namely the Chief Executive, Deputy Chief Executive, Finance Director, Medical Director and Nursing Director apply for their posts in the usual way. They are then short-listed for interview by the Board but with an assessor from the Welsh Assembly Government on the panel. Key interest groups – the local population, local authorities and the clinicians are mostly excluded. This is seen, by some, as a disadvantage and the fact that the Board is wholly appointed contravenes Aneurin Bevan's maxim that *"election is a better principle than selection."*

The Clinical Directorate structure introduced by the 1990 reforms does mean that in addition to delivering high standards of patient care clinicians are required to manage the resources devoted to their own activities and does, of course, give them an opportunity to decide on priorities. However, Chief Executives are in a vulnerable position, with a high casualty rate, and it remains to be seen whether government-appointed Boards will support clinicians when disputes arise.

The Carmarthenshire NHS Trust now appears to be going from strength to strength and the efforts of its 3,200 able and dedicated staff are much appreciated by the population it serves. The provision of services at its two acute hospitals awaits rationalisation. In 2002/2003 the Trust treated 55,910 inpatients (including Day Cases), 190,639 outpatients and 58,152 new Accident & Emergency patients. Operating expenses were £110.790 million with a retained deficit of £4.487 million. Waiting lists for outpatient appointments and for treatment remain unacceptably high although each year sees some reduction in waiting time. Most specialties are represented except those that require a catchment population of, at least, one million to operate economically and to generate enough patients to maintain the skills of the providers. Radiotherapy & Oncology patients are referred to Singleton Hospital, Swansea. Invasive Cardiology, Cardiac Surgery, Interventional Radiology, Neurology and Neurosurgery, Oral & Maxillofacial Surgery, Neonatal & Paediatric Surgery and Plastic & Burns Surgery are provided at Morriston Hospital, Swansea which is also designated a major trauma centre. For the convenience of patients a number of joint clinics are held at the Trust's hospitals by visiting Consultants. The Trust plans to build a new Accident & Emergency Department at Glangwili at a cost of £3.3 million because the present facility, opened in 1960, is now quite unsuitable for its purpose.[24]

The Wanless Reports (2002 & 2004), commissioned by Prime Minister, Tony Blair, Chancellor, Gordon Brown and Health Secretary, then Alan Milburn now Patricia Hewitt, make gloomy reading. The acute sector of the NHS is still characterised by shortage of funds, lack of investment in high technology and IT, lack of highly skilled staff, outdated facilities, lack of evidence-based treatments, poor data collection, waste, waiting lists and grannies on trolleys. It is not obvious, however, that other countries have a better answer.[11] Healthcare planning, as the Reports emphasise, is immensely complex and must take account of changing demographics and needs, technological advance, cost, productivity, availability of skilled staff and public expectations.[30,31]

The Review of Health and Social Care in Wales (2003), advised by Derek Wanless, and commissioned by the Welsh Assembly Government, reveals an even grimmer picture. Life expectancy, mortality and key survival rates in Wales are worse than United Kingdom averages which do not compare favourably with some other developed countries. It concludes that the NHS may be unsustainable in its present form although efforts are being made in Whitehall and in Cardiff to implement the Reports' recommendations which focus on individual responsibility particularly for a healthy lifestyle, public health, preventive medicine, screening and the community.[32]

Thus it seems that frequent reorganisations of the NHS, with the addition and subtraction of layers of managers, have had little effect on hospital efficiency. There is no incentive for NHS staff to achieve private sector efficiency if they get paid the same however many patients they manage per day. Demand remains insatiable with medical science continuing to produce new and very expensive equipment and treatments. It seems unreasonable to expect clinicians to take responsibility for rationing. However, it is quite possible that, a few decades from now, the way in which acute-care medicine is practised and healthcare delivered will be unrecognisable to today's healthcare professionals. Today's General Practitioner may eventually disappear with most primary and routine secondary care being provided by nurse and other registered practitioners such as physician's assistants. Physicians and surgeons are likely to provide only the most novel and complex treatments in narrow sub-specialties and undertake research and development. Some believe that perhaps, in the future, surgery will only need to be performed for trauma and simple mechanical disorders.

Recent studies have shown that there is only a tenuous connection between a nation's expenditure on its healthcare system and the health status of its population.[12] Most of an individual's total healthcare costs are incurred in the final 3 years of life. Healthcare's contribution to the reduction in mortality rates since 1948 is mainly attributable to immunisation programmes and the treatment of infectious diseases with antibiotics. Life expectancy is correlated with income per capita but not to the numbers of doctors, hospital beds or health expenditure. Indeed, quite remarkably it has been shown that operation rates for particular conditions are related more to the number of specialists than to any measure of clinical need.[11] Paradoxically, supply appears to drive demand and there is little evidence that populations receiving aggressive care live longer.[11] In 2001, Cynthia Ramsay compared the healthcare systems in 8 countries; Australia, Canada, Germany, Singapore, South Africa, Switzerland, the United Kingdom and the United States. She concluded that the best way forward is for governments to ensure access to, and the availability of, preventive and basic primary care. Public health – access to sanitation, safe water, immunization, and screening services some of which await an evidence base – still seems to have a positive effect on health status. Beyond public health governments should perhaps focus on ensuring access to healthcare for those that cannot afford to pay, just as the founders of the Infirmary wished to do in the 19th century, and perhaps requiring their citizens to insure against catastrophic illness.[12]

Enthusiastic volunteers, both medical and lay, have been the essential links in the chain from arranging for the use of the old Borough Gaol as the first dedicated hospital in Carmarthen to the opening of a modern structure of steel, concrete and glass which continues to acquire all the latest developments in medical science and technology more than 150 years later. This voluntary tradition is continued today by the League of Friends of the West Wales General Hospital one of the oldest such organisations in the country established in 1948. The League has raised and spent hundreds of thousands of pounds since 1948 on equipment and amenities for patients. The Women's Royal

Voluntary Service (WRVS) set up their first canteen in Glangwili in 1952 and have continued ever since. Perhaps today's young people, as they grow older, will come to appreciate that the resources of the State are limited and will ensure that this vital voluntary service is continued. However, at the time of writing the younger generation appears to have embraced the left-wing doctrine that the State is solely responsible for its citizens from "cradle to grave" and, disappointingly, show little interest in such historic and worthwhile activities.

References:

[1] Problems of Social Policy, R. M. Titmuss, HMSO, 1950.

[2] Ministry of Health, Consultative Council on Medical and Allied Services, Interim Report on the Future Provision of Medical and Allied Services (Chairman, Lord Dawson), Cmd 693, HMSO, 1920.

[3] Ministry of Health, Final Report of the Voluntary Hospitals Commission (Chairman, Lord Cave), Cmd 1335 HMSO, 1921.

[4] Parliament: Report on Social Insurance & Allied Services (Chairman, Sir William Beveridge), Cmd 6040 HMSO, 1942.

[5] Ministry of Health, Report of the Office Committee on the "Demobilisation" of the Emergency Hospital Scheme, Ministry of Health, 1943.

[6] Ministry of Health White Paper, A National Health Service, Cmd 6502 HMSO, 1944.

[7] The Hospitals – 1800 to 1948, A Study in Social Administration, in England and Wales, Brian Abel-Smith, 1964, Harvard University Press.

[8] A General Medical Service for the Nation, British Medical Association, 1938, London.

[9] Proposals for a General Medical Service for the Nation, British Medical Association, 1929, London.

[10] A Plan for British Hospitals, Stephen Taylor, Lancet, 28th October, 1939, London

[11] From Cradle to Grave. Fifty Years of the NHS, Geoffrey Rivett, 1997, Kings Fund Publishing.

[12] Beyond the public-private debate. An examination of quality, access and cost in the healthcare systems of eight countries Cynthia Ramsay for the Marigold Foundation, Calgary, Western Sky Communications Ltd., Vancouver, July, 2001.

[13] Ministry of Health, Hospital Survey- the hospital services of South Wales, HMSO, 1945.

[14] Annual Reports, County Infirmary, Carmarthen, 1847 to 1942, Carmarthenshire Archives Service.

[15] Captain K. J. Gale, R.A., Adjutant, 1945 to 1947, Carmarthen Military Hospital, Personal communication, April, 1967.

[16] Annual Reports, West Wales Hospital Management, 1948 to 1963, Carmarthenshire Archives Service.

[17] Ministry of Health. Report for the year 1955, Cmd 9857, HMSO, 1956.

[18] National Health Service, A Hospital Plan for England and Wales, Cmd 1604, HMSO, 1962.

[19] Annual Reports, South West Wales Hospital Management Committee, 1963 to 1972, Carmarthenshire Archives Service.

[20] Annual Report, Dyfed Area Health Authority, 1974/75, Carmarthenshire Archives Service.

[21] Royal Commission on the National Health Service, Cmd 7615, HMSO, 1979.

[22] Annual Report, East Dyfed Health Authority, 1988/89, Carmarthenshire Archives Service.

[23] Annual Reports, Carmarthen & District NHS Trust, West Wales General Hospital.

[24] Annual Reports, Carmarthenshire NHS Trust, West Wales General Hospital.

[25] Report by Auditor General for Wales presented to the National Assembly for Wales on the 5th July, 2002, National Audit Office for Wales.

[26] Investigation into Carmarthenshire NHS Trust. Report to the Assembly Minister for Health and Social Services, National Assembly of Wales. Commission for Health Improvement, 2000 & 2002.

[27] Evaluating the Quality of Medical Care, Avedis Donabedian, Milbank Memorial Fund Quarterly, 1966, 44: 166 - 206.

[28] Explorations in Quality Assessment and Monitoring, Avedis Donabedian, Ann Arbor, Health Administration Press, 1985.

[29] First Report of the Joint Working Party on the Organisation of Medical Work in Hospital, Ministry of Health, London, HMSO 1967.

[30] Securing our Future Health: Taking a Long Term View, Derek Wanless, April, 2002, HMSO 2002

[31] Securing Good Health for the Whole Population, Derek Wanless, February, 2004, HMSO, 2004.

[32] Review of Health & Social Care in Wales (advised by Derek Wanless), June 2003, Welsh Assembly Government, 2003.

BIBLIOGRAPHY

Abel-Smith, Brian: The Hospitals - 1800 to 1948, A Study in Social Administration in England & Wales, Heinemann, 1964, Harvard University Press, 1964.

Abel-Smith, Brian: A History of the Nursing Profession, Heinemann, 1960, Harvard University Press, 1960.

Buck, A.H.: The Growth of Medicine from the Earliest Times to 1800, Yale University Press, 1917, The Dawn of Modern Medicine, Yale University Press, 1920.

Clark-Kennedy, A.E.: The London: A Study in the Voluntary Hospital System, 2 vols., Pitman Medical Publishing Company, London, 1961 & 1963.

Cope, Sir Zachary: Florence Nightingale and the Doctors, Museum Press, London, 1958.

Dainton, Courtney: The Story of England's Hospitals, Museum Press, London, 1961.

Fox, Margaret E.: First Steps in Nursing, 2nd Edition, Scientific Press, London, 1924.

Guthrie, Douglas: A History of Medicine, Nelson, London, 1945.

Leff, S & V.: From Witchcraft to World Health, Lawrence & Wishart, London, 1956.

Lodwick, Victor & Joyce: The Story of Carmarthen, St. Peter's Press, Carmarthen, 1994.

Morris, Sir Ernest: A History of The London Hospital, Arnold, 1926.

Nightingale, Florence: Notes on Hospitals, 1859, British Library, London, Notes on Lying-In Institutions, 1871, British Library, London.

Lives of the Fellows, 1800 to 2002, Library of the Royal College of Surgeons of England.

Power, Sir D'Arcy: Editor, Masters of British Medicine, 1936. A Short History of Surgery, 1933. British Library, London.

Pavey, Agnes: The Story of the Growth of Nursing as an Art, a Vocation And a Profession, Faber & Faber, 1938

Rivett, Geoffrey C.: From Cradle to Grave, Fifty Years of the NHS, King's Fund Publishing, 1997.

Spurrell, William: Carmarthen and its Neighbourhood, Notes Topical & Historical, 1879, Facsimile Reprint Dyfed County Council Cultural Department, 1995.

Tooley, S.: The History of Nursing in the British Empire, Bonsfield, London, 1906.

Williams, David: Modern Wales, University of Wales Press,1950.

Williams, David: The Rebecca Riots, University of Wales Press, 1955.

Williams, John ab Ithel & Pughe John: The Physicians of Myddfai, Or the Medical Practice of the Celebrated Rhiwallon and His Sons, of Myddfai, in Carmarthenshire, 1861, Facsimile Reprint, 1993, Llanerch Press.

INDEX

Abel-Smith, Professor Brian, 6-7, 17, 173, 199
American Military Hospital & Prisoner-of-War Hospital, Carmarthen, 91-3, 201-3
Banting, Frederick, Nobel Laureate, 120
Barnard, Christian, 122
Barracks, Carmarthen, 27
Best, Charles, Nobel Laureate, 120
Beveridge Report, 1942, 198
Black Book of Carmarthen, 2
Black Friars of Carmarthen, 2
Blair, Tony, Prime Minister, 218
Borough Surveyor, Collard, E.C., 22, 29, 36
Bowen, Dr. John, 23,25
British Medical Association, 154, 198-9
British Nurses Association, 84-5
British Red Cross Society, 157-8, 167
Brown, Rev. Canon C.G., 134, 158-60
Burke & Hare, 17
Calman Report, 127
Carmarthenshire County Council,
Local Government Act, 1929, 148-9, 173
Penlan Workhouse, 148-9
Medical Officer of Health, 174
Castle Hill House, 1 Spilman St., 115-16
CAT scanning, 122
Cave Report, 1921, 161-2, 197-8
Cawdor, Earl, 22
Chamberlain, Neville, Prime Minister, 117
Churchill, Winston, Prime Minister, 198
Cochrane, Professor Sir Archibald, 126
College of Nursing, 84-5
Company of Grocers, 6
Company of Surgeons, 6
Cooper, Sir Astley, FRCS., 17
County Gaol, 7-8
County Isolation Hospital, Upper Tumble, 175
Crick, Sir Francis, Nobel Laureate, 120-1
Curie, Marie, Nobel Laureate, 168
Curtiss, Lawrence, 121
Davies, Glanmore R. MD, FRCP., 125
Davies, Mrs. Laura, 86-8
Davy, Sir Humphrey, 18
Dawson of Penn Report, 1920, 197-8
Ditcham, Matron Linda, 83-6
Dispensary, Carmarthen, 24
Dissolution of the Monasteries, 2
District Nursing, 94
Donabedian, Dr. Avedis, 216
Donaldson, Sir Liam, 128
Dynevor, Lord, 21-3
Evans, Alcwyn C., 41
Fenwick, Mrs Bedford, 84-5
Fibiger, Dr. Johannes, Nobel Laureate, 126
First World War, 157-65
Freemasons, 39-40
Furnace House, St. Peter's St., 115-16
German Field Marshals, 203
Godber, Sir George, 217
Grey Friars of Carmarthen, 2
Guild of Pepperers, 6
Guild of Surgeons, 5
Hartland, Matron Dorothy, 86, 88-9
Health Visitors, 94
Healy, Dr. James J., 86, 114-17, 119-120
Holloway, Thomas "Professor", 15-16
Horowitz, Basil, 121
Houndsfield, Sir Godfrey, Nobel Laureate, 122
Howard, John, Prison Reformer, 8
Hughes, John, FRCS., 11, 112-13
Hywel Dda, 2-3
Infirmary,
Ambulance, 169-72
Borough Gaol, 8, 28-9, 33-6
Carmarthen Union, 148-9
Children, 167-8
Contributory Schemes, 179-81
Closure of acute services, 210
Closure and sale, 1996, 214
Development, 165-72
Effects of First World War, 151-65
Employers & Public Authorities, 148-50
Expansion, 173-79
First World War, 157-61
Foundation, 1, 21-31
Fund Raising, 143-7
Governors, 130
House Committee, 130
Laying of Foundation Stone, 39-44
Linen League, 137-8
Maternity Department, 173-9
Matrons, 79-80, 82-4, 92-3
National Insurance, 153-7
"New", 36-46
Nursing Profession, 72-99
Nurses Hostel, 167

Obstetrics, 173-4
Private Patients, 150-2
Radium, 168-9
Rules & Regulations, 72-6, 101-07, 138-43, 151
Second World War, 117-9, 198
Subscriptions, 130-2, 147-8
Surgical Treatment and Outcomes, 107-8
Visitors of the Week, 135-7
Workmen's Collections, 152
X-rays, 166
Island Farm Special Camp 11, Bridgend, 203
Ivy Bush Royal Hotel, 9
James, J.R.E. FRCOG., 115
Jenner, Edward, 12
Joint Commission for the Accreditation of Healthcare Organizations, 216
Jones, Rev. D. Latimer Maurice, Vicar of St. Peter's Church, 111, 137-8, 139, 141
Jones, Major Francis, 2
King's Fund, 216
Lauterbur, Paul, Nobel Laureate, 122
Lawrence, Dr. Henry, 24-5, 28, 100, 111, 113
League of Friends, 146, 220
Lewis, Rev. Waldo, 203
Liston, Sir Robert, FRCS, 18
Lloyd-George, Rt. Hon. David, 153-4
Long, Dr. Crawford, 18
Lister, Sir Joseph (Lord), 18-19
Maliphant, Dr. Henry B., 124-5
Mansel, Sir John, 24-5
Mansfield, Sir Peter, Nobel Laureate, 122
Medical Profession,
Anaesthesia, 18, 117
Appraisal, 128
Barbers Company, 5
Barber-Surgeons Company, 5-6
Chloroform, 18, 108
Clinical Directorates, 217-18
Clinical Governance, 216-17
"Cogwheel" Godber Report, 217
Continuing Medical Education, 127
Ether, 18
Evidence-based Medicine, 126, 215-17
Future of medical practice, 219
Gangrene, "Hospital", 18
General Medical Council, 6, 127-8
Health Status of Population, 220
Laparoscopic Surgery, 123
Life expectancy in Carmarthen, 21-2
Medical Officer of Health, 21-2
Medical Registration Act, 1858, 6
Medical Schools, 126
Medical Science, advances in, 120-3
Medical treatment in the 19th century, 109
Multi-Disciplinary Teams, 101, 216
Mystique of Medical Practice, 125
Placebo effect, 125
Public Health, Carmarthen, 21-2. 211-12
Quality Assurance, 215-16
Randomised Controlled Trials, 126
Revalidation, 128
Royal Colleges, foundation of, 5
Surgery in the 19th century, 107-8
Todd Report, 1966, 126
Millard, A. Henry, FRCS, 124
Ministry of Health,
Emergency Medical Service, 1939, 117-19, 198
Inception of, 161
Hospital Survey, South Wales, 1945, 201
A Hospital Plan for England and Wales, 1962, 207-8
Morris, T.C. of Brynmyrddin, 13, 23, 133
Morris, William, 23, 133
Morriston Hospital, Swansea, 122, 218
Morton, Dr. William, 18
Mouret, Philippe, 123
Murray, Dr. Joseph, FACS, Nobel Laureate, 120
Myddfai, Physicians of, 3-5
Napoleonic Wars, 10
Nash, John, Architect, 8
National Health Service,
Bevan, Rt.Hon. Aneurin, 198
Carmarthen & District NHS Trust, 213
Carmarthenshire NHS Trust, 214-15, 218
Carmarthen/Dinefwr Health Management Unit, 211
Commission for Health Improvement, (Healthcare Commission, 2004), 215
Dyfed Area Health Authority, 210-11
Dyfed Powys Health Authority, 213
East Dyfed District Health Authority, 211
Foundation of, 1, 119-20, 198-9
Future of, 218-21
Local Health Boards, 21, 213
National Institute for Clinical Excellence, 215
NHS & Community Care Act, 1990, 212
Private Sector Efficiency, 219
Reorganisation, 210-13

  South West Wales Hospital Management Committee, 208, 210
  Trust Boards, 217-18
  Wanless Reports, England & Wales, 218-19
  West Wales Hospital Management Committee, 203-4

NHS White Paper, 1998, 214
National Insurance Act, 1911, 153-4
Nightingale, Florence, 43-4, 80-1, 84
Nissen Huts, Glangwili, 91, 202
Nott, General Sir William, 23
"Nott" Infirmary, 23
Nursing Profession, 72-99
  19th century reform movement, 80-2
  Academic nurses, 95-9
  Briggs Report, 94-5
  District Nurses, 94
  General Nursing Council, 84-5, 90, 94
  Male Nurses, 91
  Midwifery, 93, 173-5
  Nurses' Lectures, 83, 88
  Nurse Practitioners, 98, 219
  Nursing etiquette, 89
  Nursing & Midwifery Council, 95
  Nursing Process, 97
  Project 2000, 96
  Rivett, Dr. Geoffrey, 98-9, 212
  Salmon Report, 94
  School of Nursing at Trinity College, 95
  State Enrolled Nurses, 90, 96
  State Registered Nurses, 84-5
  Superannuation, 90
  United Kingdom Central Council for Nursing, Midwifery & Health Visiting, 95

Parry, Rev. Canon, A.W., 178
Pasteur, Professor Louis, 19
PET scanning, 122-3
Philipps, Sir Grismond, 24
Phillips, Professor Miles, 115, 118
Poor Laws,
  Amendment Act, 1834, 10
  Board of Guardians, Carmarthen, 11-12
  Borough Gaol or Bridewell, 8, 28-9
  Carmarthen Union Workhouse, Penlan, 9-15, 28, 148-9
  Chaplain, Carmarthen Union, 149
  Local Government Act, 1929, 148-9
  Medical Officers, 8-9, 11-12
  Workhouse mortality rate, 14,
  Pauperism in Carmarthen, 8-11, 22
  Relieving Officer, 11
  Tudor Poor Law Act, 1576, 7
  St. Peter's Parish Surgeon, 8-9, 12
  St. Peter's Vestry Poorhouse, 7-10

Prince Philip Hospital, Llanelly, 214-15
Queen Victoria, 18, 23
Queen Elizabeth Endowed Grammar School, Carmarthen, 36-7
Quarter Sessions, Carmarthen, 21
Ramsay, Cynthia, Health Economist, 220
Rebecca Riots, 12-13, 23
Red Book of Hergest, 3
Rees, Richard L., FRCS, 120, 125
Rice-Trevor, Colonel George, 23-5, 27-8
Richards, H. Brinley, 45, 145-6
Rivett, Dr. Geoffrey, 98-9, 212
Roentgen, Professor Wilhelm, 166
Rogers, D.T.P., MBE., 214
Rowlands, James, FRCS, 113
Royal College of Nursing, 84-5
Royal College of Physicians of London, 5-6
Royal College of Surgeons of England, 5
St. Peter's Church, 2
Semmelweiss, Dr. Ignaz, 18
Simons, William, 23
Singleton Hospital, Swansea, 122-3
Simpson, Sir James (Lord), 18-19
Stacey, Edmund Hills, MRCS, 100, 112
Starzl, Thomas, FACS, 122
Thatcher, Margaret, Prime Minister, 212
Thirlwall, Dr. Connop, Bishop of St. David's, 25, 39, 43-4, 149-50
School of Nursing,
  Infirmary, 83-5, 88, 90
  West Wales General Hospital, 93-4
  Trinity College, 95
  University of Wales, Swansea, 96-7
  "All-graduate" profession, 97-9

St. David's Hospital,
  Joint Counties Lunatic Asylum, 22

Trevor-Jones, Dr. Alan, 176-7, 201
Vaughan-Jones, Matron Arfona, 92-3
Voluntary Hospitals, 16-17, 161-2, 198
Watson, James, Nobel Laureate, 120-1
West Wales General Hospital, 197-222
  Acquisition of Glangwili site, 201-2
  Construction, 206-10
  Development, 212-13
  General Nursing Council, 84-5, 90, 94
  League of Friends, 146, 220

Matron's rounds, 92
Minister of Health, 206
New wards, 91-2
Nursing staff, 60-61
Orthopaedic traction, 125
Priory Day Hospital, 213-14
Queen Elizabeth, the Queen Mother, 207
School of Nursing, 93
War Office & Delegation, 202, 206
West Wales Sanatorium for Tuberculosis, 175
Williams, David C., MCh., FRCS, 125
Women's Royal Voluntary Service, 220-1